CW00675974

Oil & Gas
Digital Transformation

Fawziya Thurayya Arian

Abstract

The immature advanced digitalization in the oil and gas industry can limit access to the potential value of mature progressive digitalization. Oil and gas leaders must expedite the implementation of advanced digitalization to increase organizational proficiencies and reduce costs and losses. Grounded in Pettigrew and Whipp's dimensions of strategic change theory, the purpose of this qualitative multiple case study was to explore strategies some leaders in the oil and gas industry used to implement advanced digitalization. The participants were seven leaders in two oil service companies in North America involved in the successful implementation of progressive digitalization. Data were collected using semistructured interviews and public documents from participating companies and analyzed using Groenewald's thematic analysis. Six themes emerged: advanced digitalization strategies, environmental assessment, resources, linking strategic and operational changes, leading change, and overall coherence. A key recommendation for oil and gas leaders is to adopt a dynamic strategy accounting for all involved stakeholders and aligned with the fast-changing environment in advanced digitalization. The implications for positive social change include the potential increase of advanced digitalization use in the oil and gas industry, possibly resulting in more job opportunities, reducing job stress, and improving the local economy and level of prosperity.

Dedication

I dedicate this study to my mother, Nasrin Nobakht, my late father, Mohammad T. Rezafar, my brother Amir H. Rezafar, and my sister Elham Rezafar. I also devote this research to my husband, Payam Pirouzan, and our sons, Aran Pirouzan and Radan Pirouzan, who encouraged me on this journey with their inspiration, support, and confidence.

Acknowledgments

I am thankful for the guidance of my chair, Dr. Alexandre Y. Lazo, whose patience and direction helped me refine my thoughts and stay focused throughout my doctoral journey. I would also like to thank Dr. Scott Hipsher, Dr. Edward Walker, Dr. Diane Dusick, and Dr. Denise Land for their reassurance and valued feedback throughout the process. In addition, I would like to thank the faculty, staff, and fellow scholars who kept me motivated in this venture.

Table of Contents

List of Tables iv

List of Figures vi

Section 1: Foundation of the Study 1

Background of the Problem 1

Problem Statement 2

Purpose Statement 3

Nature of the Study 3

Research Question 4

Interview Questions 5

Conceptual Framework 5

Operational Definitions 6

Assumptions, Limitations, and Delimitations 7

Assumptions 7

Limitations 8

Delimitations 9

Significance of the Study 9

Value to Business 10

Contribution to Business Practice 10

Implications for Social Change 11

A Review of the Professional and Academic Literature 11

Strategic Change Theory 14

i

Environmental Assessment... 17

Required Resources (Structure, Process, People)................................. 25

Linking Strategic and Operational Changes 31

Leading Advanced Digitalization Change.. 36

Overall Coherence of Advanced Digitalization.................................... 40

Transition 41

Section 2: The Project...43

Purpose Statement..43

Role of the Researcher 43

Participants..45

Research Method and Design 46

Research Method 46

Research Design... 47

Population and Sampling 49

Ethical Research..51

Data Collection Instruments 53

Data Collection Technique 55

Data Organization Technique 57

Data Analysis..57

Reliability and Validity...59

Reliability.. 59

Validity 60

Transition and Summary...62

Section 3: Application to Professional Practice and Implications for Change.................63

Introduction...63

Presentation of the Findings...64

    Emergent Theme 1: Advanced Digitalization Strategies.................................... 65

    Emergent Theme 2: Environment Assessment.. 69

    Emergent Theme 3: Advanced Digitalization Resources 71

    Emergent Theme 4: Linking Strategic and Operational Changes of

        Advanced Digitalization 73

    Emergent Theme 5: Leading Advanced Digitalization in the Oil and Gas

        Industry 76

    Emergent Theme 6: Overall Coherence of Advanced Digital in the Oil and

        Gas Industry 78

Applications to Professional Practice 80

Implications for Social Change...81

Recommendations for Action 81

Recommendations for Further Research...82

Reflections 83

Conclusion 84

List of Tables

Table 1. Classification Matrix: Alignment to the Walden DBA Rubric for

    Recency of Articles...13

Table 2. Classification Matrix: Alignment to Walden DBA Rubric for Peer-

    Reviewed Articles..14

Table 3. Strategic Framework of Germany's Industry 4.0 24

Table 4. Emergent Theme 1: Number of Times Advanced Digitalization

    Strategies Discussed..66

Table 5. Emergent of Subcategories for Theme 1 67

Table 6. Emergent Theme 2: Number of Times Environmental Assessment

    Discussed 69

Table 7. Emergent of Subcategories for Theme 2 70

Table 8. Emergent Theme 3: Number of Times Advanced Digitalization

    Resources Discussed..71

Table 9. Emergent of Subcategories for Theme 3 72

Table 10. Emergent Theme 4: Number of Times Linking Strategic and

    Operational Changes Discussed...73

Table 11. Emergent of Subcategories for Theme 4 74

Table 12. Emergent Theme 5: Number of Times Leading Advance Digitalization

    in the Oil and Gas Industry Discussed...76

Table 13. Emergent of Subcategories for Theme 5 77

Table 14. Emergent Theme 6: Number of Times Overall Coherence of Advance

Digitalization in the Oil and Gas Industry Discussed..78

Table 15. Emergent of Subcategories for Theme 6: Number of Times Different

Subcategories for Theme 6 Emerged in Relation with the Number of

Participants Discussed Those Subcategories..79

List of Figures

Figure 1. Word Cloud of Frequency Query Result from the Interviews 65

Section 1: Foundation of the Study

With the fourth industrial revolution, advanced digitalization has progressed

substantially (Dalenogare et al., 2018; Deif & Vivek, 2022; Lu et al., 2019a; Lu et al.,

2019b). Though the importance of advanced digitalization is evident in business

environments of the second decade of the 21st century, some sectors have had less

progress than others. The oil and gas industry is on the list of sectors with low

momentum in advanced digitalization (Lu et al., 2019a). The aim of this study was to

explore ways to improve the onboarding of advanced digitalization in the oil and gas

industry, learning from the thriving industries and companies in Industry 4.0.

Background of the Problem

Oil prices declined from over $100 per barrel in 2014 to half in 2015 (Baumeister

& Kilian, 2016; Baumeister et al., 2018; Stocker et al., 2018), and oil prices remained

low, at around $30 per barrel, in 2020. The macroeconomic variables and supply and

demand in the integrated global oil market have had negative effects on oil prices

(Herrera et al., 2019). For example, the stock markets and the financial performance of

European oil and gas firms have deteriorated because of the low prices of oil (Bagirov &

Mateus, 2019). For any sudden increase in the activities in the oil and gas industry, more

workforce, financial, and technological capabilities such as robotics and advanced

digitalization are needed (Chen et al., 2014). Applying new technology to drilling tools in

the oil industry is common (Ma et al., 2015). Nevertheless, modern technology and

advanced digitalization are neither synonymous nor mutually exclusive. There has been

some progress in developing reliable advanced digitalization systems enabling remote operations on an unmanned oil and gas facility (Anisi & Skourup, 2012).

Industries like aviation, manufacturing, and healthcare have had more progress in advanced digitalization compared to the oil and gas industry. As an example in aviation, human–robot collaboration through the application of a hand-guided collaborative robot in the final stages of aircraft assembly is a relief for the workers from high mental and physical labor (Meibner et al., 2018). In the medical industry, the human–robot interfacing technology in health care has increased, providing a powerful tool for patients' rehabilitation, assistive, and independent living (Pang et al., 2018). This study may be used as a reference for the oil and gas industry leaders in exploring ways to improve the onboarding of advanced digitalization.

Problem Statement

The oil and gas industry is in the Oil and Gas 4.0 era, inspired by the Industry 4.0 concept, resulting in the promotion of advanced digitalization, including but not limited to social, mobile, analytics, and cloud, to achieve higher value (Lu et al., 2019a; Toma & Popa, 2018). But the advanced digitalization process in the oil and gas industry has been slow, at only 4.68 out of 10, classifying the industry under the developing group on advanced digitalization maturity (Lu et al., 2019a). The general business problem is the immature advanced digitalization in the oil and gas industry, limiting accessibility to the potential value of mature advanced digitalization. The specific business problem is that some leaders in the oil and gas industry lack successful strategies to implement advanced digitalization.

Purpose Statement

The purpose of this qualitative multiple case study was to explore successful strategies some leaders in the oil and gas industry used to implement advanced digitalization. The target population was a minimum of four leaders in at least two companies, preferably one oil service company and one oil company in North America, who successfully created and utilized advanced digitalization in the oil and gas industry. This study may lead to a positive social change by encouraging advanced digitalization in the oil and gas industry, resulting in the creation of more job opportunities for the local workers and companies, reducing job stress, and improving the domestic economy and level of prosperity.

Nature of the Study

The selected research method for this study was qualitative. The qualitative method is suitable for a broad context of a business problem, analyzing the data from direct fieldwork observations for exploring contemporary, real-life situations to understand a phenomenon through in-depth, open-ended interviews and written documents (Antwi & Hamza, 2015; Runfola et al., 2017). The focus of this study was on exploring successful strategies some leaders in the oil and gas industry could use to implement advanced digitalization. Therefore, the qualitative method was applicable. The quantitative method was unsuitable because it is used for defining the relationship between selected variables by analyzing numerical data utilizing statistical techniques and testing hypotheses focusing on closed-ended questions (Cronin, 2014; Marshall & Rossman, 2016; Watson, 2015). The mixed-method approach is a combination of qualitative and quantitative methods, producing an overall outcome with more extensive information (Marshall & Rossman, 2016). The mixed-method approach was not an option, as quantitative data could not help address the purpose of the study.

The multiple case study design is suitable for studying advanced digitalization in the oil and gas industry as a contemporary phenomenon in more than one company. In a case study, the researcher investigates a recent phenomenon in a real-life context with an in-depth, descriptive, and exploratory analysis (Yin, 2018). In the multiple case study, researchers explore details and perspectives concerning a specific situation replicated in more than one case, offering more reliable outcomes (Yin, 2018). Phenomenology is the description of human beings' experience of a phenomenon while setting aside bias in the process (Katsirikou & Lin, 2017), but advanced digitalization was the focus of the study as opposed to the experience of individuals. The narrative design is the description of an individual's story from their own life experience (Marshall & Rossman, 2016). However, advanced digitalization strategies had only been recently implemented in some companies in the oil and gas industry. Finally, ethnography is the direct observation of participants' social interactions, behaviors, and perceptions in their groups, organizations, and communities (Ingold, 2014; Mannay & Morgan, 2015). This research was about successful strategies for advanced digitalization in the oil and gas industry instead of people's perceptions of advanced digitalization.

Research Question

One overarching research question guided the study: What successful advanced digitalization strategies can leaders in the oil and gas industry use to implement digitalization?

Interview Questions

1. What successful advanced digitalization strategies have you used?

2. Why do you consider your advanced digitalization strategies effective?

3. What barriers did you face while advanced digitalizing, and how did you address them?

4. What is the percentage of advanced digitalization in your current job, and what percentage do you think it should be in the next 5 years?

5. What resources are essential for advanced digitalization?

6. How do you ensure the commitment of users toward advanced digitalization?

7. What additional information would you like to add regarding the strategies used for advanced digitalization?

Conceptual Framework

The conceptual framework is a lens to examine a phenomenon under study (Korstjens & Moser, 2017). In 1993, Pettigrew and Whipp established the dimensions of strategic change in their book called *Managing Change for Competitive Success* (Jelinek, 1993; Sweeney et al., 2019). The identified dimensions are (a) content, (b) process, and (c) context for strategic change. Pettigrew and Whipp considered the content to be the what, the process to be the how, and the context to be the where for the strategic change. Pettigrew and Whipp also identified five interrelated factors for successful strategic change management consisting of (a) environmental assessment, (b) resources, (c) linking strategic and operational changes, (d) leading change, and (e) overall coherence.

The concept of advanced digitalization is new to the oil and gas industry, calling for a strategic change process. Transformation of the industry from the conventional approach in drilling and completions toward an advanced digital approach may be challenging, requiring the buy-in and engagement of the stakeholders. Pettigrew and Whipp's conceptual framework for strategic change was suitable for exploring successful advanced digitalization strategies in the oil and gas industry. The dimensions resulted in the accommodation of a thorough investigation of what, how, and where for advanced digitalization in the industry. The interrelated factors for successful strategic change management help implement change in the long term.

Operational Definitions

The following operational definitions provide additional clarity on the applied terms in this doctoral study.

Advanced or progressive digitalization: The integration of digital technologies, including social, mobile, analytics, and cloud, to transform the way of working (Lu et al., 2019a). The words *automation* and *robotics* used in scholarly literature mainly had similar definitions as the advanced or progressive digitalization used in this doctoral study.

Industry 4.0: The digitalization era started in 2014 with digital business models, environments, production systems, machines, operators, products, and services interconnected in the digital scene and the related virtual representation (Alcácer & Cruz-Machado, 2019).

Oil and Gas 4.0: The era in the oil and gas industry started in 2018 in response to

Industry 4.0, accelerating the advanced digital technology to achieve higher value in the oil and gas industry (Lu et al., 2019a). The characteristics of Oil and Gas 4.0 are digitalization, automation, modularization, and intelligenization (Lu et al., 2019a). The key technologies of Oil and Gas 4.0 are big data, industrial internet of things (IIoT), digital twin, wireless communication technologies, augmented reality and wearable devices, blockchain technology, and other technologies such as the autonomous robot, 3D printing, cybersecurity, and system integration (Lu et al., 2019a).

Oil companies and oil service companies: The three major actors in the oil and gas industry are: (a) the upstream petroleum companies called oil companies or operators, (b) the petroleum supply companies named oil service companies, and (c) the public sector organizations, regulating and supporting the industry (Thune et al., 2018).

Onshore and offshore: The two main categories of oil and gas facilities considering the facility's location are either on land called onshore or in water called offshore (Shukla & Karki, 2016a). The oil and gas fields located underwater are offshore fields divided into shallow-water areas or deep-water areas (Shukla & Karki, 2016b).

Assumptions, Limitations, and Delimitations

Assumptions

Assumptions are the statements accepted by the researcher as true in the study without any evidence, proof, or verification (Fan, 2013; Yin, 2018). The researcher must consider assumptions in developing the findings and inferences of the research (Grant, 2014). There were five primary assumptions for this study: (a) The selected companies would authorize their employees to participate in the interviews, (b) the participants would not have any motivation to influence the outcome of the research, (c) the participants' responses would be honest and reliable to the interview questions, (d) I would understand and capture the participants' responses effectively without any biases, and (e) I would be capable of analyzing the obtained data and establishing the patterns and themes contributing to a correct outcome.

Limitations

Limitations are potential weaknesses beyond the researcher's control that could restrict the research findings (Fan, 2013; Marshall & Rossman, 2016). The main limitation was the recency of advanced digitalization in the oil and gas industry, restricting the availability of related information and potential participants for the interview process. One of the study limitations was the number of qualified companies for participation that authorized their employees' involvement. This limitation had a more substantial effect on the oil companies' potential participants, as they could not get approval from their respective companies to attend the interviews due to data tightness. The next limitation was the restriction in sharing data because of the confidentiality of data in the oil and gas industry corporations. This limitation might have affected the openness and reliability of the participants in the interviews. Another limitation in this research was associated with me as a novice researcher handling the recent phenomenon of advanced digitalization in the oil and gas industry. Additionally, my experience in the mentioned industry might have introduced a biased overview regardless of how conscious I remained about it.

Delimitations

Delimitations are the attributes regulating the scope and outlining the boundaries

of research (Fan, 2013; Yin, 2018). The study was delimited to advanced digitalization

leaders in the oil and gas industry with successful strategies in adopting digital solutions

in their respective organizations in both oil and oil service companies. Smaller participant

groups could be consistent with the focus of qualitative research (Etz & Arroyo, 2015). I

interviewed advanced digitalization leaders in oil service companies. But I had no

success interviewing anyone in oil companies regardless of the invitations the oil

companies' potential participants received for the interview. Another delimitation of the

study was the geographical location of the research in North America, excluding other

geographic areas where advanced digitalization was being implemented.

Significance of the Study

In the second decade of the 21st century, the adoption of advanced digitalization

in different sectors such as in medical, aviation, and manufacturing industries is universal

(Alcácer & Cruz-Machado, 2019; Alexander et al., 2019; Pang et al., 2018). The

significance of this study could be in the potential benefits of advanced digitalization in

the oil and gas industry for improving the quality and the reliability of provided products

and services (Ibrahimov, 2018; Pang et al., 2018; Shukla & Karki, 2016a; Shukla &

Karki, 2016b). Oil prices have been significantly low since 2014 (Herrera et al., 2019).;

therefore, the reduction of profitability in the oil and gas industry has been inevitable. By

applying advanced digitalization, the cost of products and services provided to customers

may be lowered (Meibner et al., 2018). Lower costs may result in better profitability in the oil and gas industry. Therefore, the oil and gas industry leaders may benefit from having strategies to integrate advanced digitalization in their offered products and services for the customers.

Value to Business

The focus of my findings on the successful advanced digitalization strategies in the oil and gas industry ended up being mainly on the upstream oil service companies' perspective because of oil companies' lack of participation in the interviews. Even though I could not interview anyone from oil companies, I asked the oil service companies' participants to answer the interview questions from both the oil and oil service companies' perspectives. Due to the tight collaboration between the oil companies and the oil service companies in advanced digitalization, some valuable information could be available for the oil companies leaders in the findings of this study. Overall, the findings might be beneficial not only to oil service companies and oil companies but also to third-party service providers, communities, and end-users. Successful advanced digitalization strategies might effectively assist the oil and gas industry leaders in embarking on the advanced digitalization journey. Unsuccessful advanced digitalization strategies might result in irreversible outcomes, such as loss of resources and reputation.

Contribution to Business Practice

In this study, I identified some of the successful strategies the oil and gas industry leaders used toward advanced digitalization. Implementing successful advanced digitalization strategies could result in positive economic benefits while minimizing risk. Additionally, this study might further gain the trust of the companies in the oil and gas industry in adopting advanced digitalization for their operations. The strategies to improve service quality could enhance reliability and address cybersecurity vulnerabilities by providing adequate preventative measures.

Implications for Social Change

This study could result in more reliable practices in performing advanced digitalization operations in the oil and gas industry. The findings in this study could transform the oil and gas industry, resulting in more job opportunities for residents of the communities. The implications for social change could include local financial stability through strengthened business activities, resulting in improved human or social conditions by promoting the worth, dignity, and development of the individuals in the community. This study could lead to improved local lifestyles and the well-being of local communities, stimulating economic prosperity.

A Review of the Professional and Academic Literature

The purpose of a literature review was to provide an overview of the contemporary literature related to the research topic (Baker, 2016). In this section of my qualitative multiple case study, I explored and analyzed the body of literature for successful strategies that some oil and gas industry leaders had used to implement advanced digitalization. To get a comprehensive view of the successful strategies leaders used for advanced digitalization, I broadened my search to multiple industries before focusing on the oil and gas industry leaders. My multiple-industry approach allowed me to outline the successful strategies used by leaders in different sectors.

The conceptual framework I had defined for my study was Pettigrew and Whipp's theory on dimensions of strategic change. Therefore, I started my literature review by discussing and analyzing the dimensions of the strategic change theory. The rest of my literature review focused on the dimensions of the strategic change theory related to the advanced digitalization in the oil and gas industry and a few other sectors. Analyzing and synthesizing the peer-reviewed scholarly literature on advanced digitalization in different industries, I gained an overview of the successful strategies some leaders in various sectors used. Finding peer-reviewed scholarly literature on the successful strategies used by leaders in the oil and gas industry for advanced digitalization was a challenge. Nevertheless, this literature review is a reliable reference for my doctoral study data analysis.

For this literature review, I searched the peer-reviewed articles through the following databases and search engines: ABI/INFORM, ScienceDirect, Business Source Complete, Sage Premier, ProQuest, and Google Scholar. The keywords used to search the databases included *digitalization, advanced digitalization, technology, automation, robotics, and innovation, combined with the oil and gas industry, Industry 4.0, Oil and Gas 4.0, energy industry,* and *energy sector.* To identify the peer-reviewed scholarly literature for advanced digitalization in different sectors, I used the exact keywords for searching the databases without identifying the industry. I did not narrow down the search by combining strategy and leaders for the articles I searched in the oil and gas industry. Given the scarcity of literature on the topic, I aimed to extract as much literature as possible with different focuses on the advanced digitalization in the oil and gas industry.

The main sections of my literature review are (a) strategic change theory; (b) environmental assessment including regulatory, economic, and industrial; (c) required resources including structure, process, and people; (d) linking strategic and operational changes; (e) leading advanced digitalization change; and (f) overall coherence of advanced digitalization. This literature review comprised 105 articles and books, of which 87.6% (92) were peer-reviewed. The articles and books included in this literature review were 85.7% (90) published within the last 5 years of this study (from 2018 to 2022). To review the background and foundation of advanced digitalization, I included articles published before 2018. Moreover, some of the conceptual theory resources were published before 2018. The detailed alignment to the Walden DBA Rubric for articles' recency and peer-review are in Table 1 and 2, respectively.

Table 1

Classification Matrix: Alignment to the Walden DBA Rubric for Recency of Articles

Sections	>5years	≤5years	Total
Strategic Change Theory	6	5	11
Environmental Assessment (Regulatory, Economic, Industrial)	5	35	40
Required Resources (Structure, Process, People)	3	20	23
Linking Strategic and Operational Changes	1	13	14
Leading Advanced Digitalization Change	0	10	10
Overall Coherence of Advanced Digitalization	0	7	7
Total	15	90	105
Percentage	14.3%	85.7%	100%

Table 2

Classification Matrix: Alignment to Walden DBA Rubric for Peer-Reviewed Articles

Sections	Not Peer-Reviewed	Peer-Reviewed	Total
Strategic Change Theory	2	9	11
Environmental Assessment (Regulatory, Economic, Industrial)	3	37	40
Required Resources (Structure, Process, People)	3	20	23
Linking Strategic and Operational Changes	1	13	14
Leading Advanced Digitalization Change	1	9	10
Overall Coherence of Advanced Digitalization	3	4	7
Total	13	92	105
Percentage	12.4%	87.6%	100%

Strategic Change Theory

The suitable conceptual theory for this study was a theory related to adopting a strategic change in an industry. Performing strategic changes is inevitable for companies to reduce the risk of getting left behind (Åberg & Torchia, 2019). The three different perspectives in studying strategic changes are (a) deterministic perspective, considering the strategic change as an externally driven process; (b) voluntaristic perspective, considering the strategic change as a managerially determined process; and (c) dialectical perspective, considering the combination of deterministic and voluntaristic perspectives (Müller & Kunisch, 2018). The dialectical perspective, with the advantage of a more extensive overview of the strategic change, was a more comprehensive approach to studying a strategic change.

One of the frameworks with the dialectical perspective is Pettigrew and Whipp's framework. Researchers have widely used Pettigrew and Whipp's framework with three basic dimensions of the context (where), the content (what), and the process (how) for analyzing the change in organizations (Rabbani et al., 2011; Sminia, 2016; Söderlund & Pemsel, 2022; Stetler et al., 2007; Uvhagen et al., 2018). Researchers initially used Pettigrew and Whipp's framework in a retrospective analysis of strategic changes to understand competitive private sector organizations, later expanded to public sectors like health care (Stetler et al., 2007).

The basic dimensions are dynamically linked and dependent on organizational elements and processes (Klarare et al., 2020). The basic dimensions are suitable for the high-level study of strategic change. The detailed approach will add more value to a thorough analysis of a strategic change.

Apart from the basic dimensions of strategic change, the central interrelated factors for managing strategic change are part of Pettigrew and Whipp's framework (Rabbani et al., 2011). The corresponding factors contributing to an organization's effectiveness are (a) understanding the environment, (b) resources management, (c) linking strategy and operational changes, (d) leading the change process, and (e) coherence (Pettigrew & Whipp, 1993; Sminia, 2021). Applying the reviewed factors may provide a more detailed analysis in the study of the strategic change. The researcher may focus on the basic dimensions, the interrelated factors, or the combination of both, depending on the magnitude and purpose of the research (Rabbani et al., 2011).

Referring to the complexity of a strategic change process, analyzing the previously mentioned interrelated factors, with each at the same degree of importance, is critical for managing change (Pettigrew & Whipp, 1993). Considering the significance of the corresponding factors in a strategic change, the focus of this study was on the discussed factors. Strategic changes should contribute to long-term organizational performance by creating and sustaining competitive advantages (Pettigrew & Whipp, 1993). Though creating a strategic change is sometimes essential, ensuring the longevity of the change is also critical. Strategic change is a purposive change for obtaining a competitive advantage considering both internal and external environments while providing an accurate translation of the concept to actions (Pettigrew & Whipp, 1993). A strategic change will be successful by ensuring continuity and fine-tuning based on the relevant findings (Pettigrew & Whipp, 1993; Sminia, 2021).

Based on Pettigrew and Whipp's framework, change is a continuous process with an interplay between the three basic dimensions (Uvhagen et al., 2018). Change agents are responsible for constantly assessing and adjusting the change process to reach the planned outcome (Uvhagen et al., 2018). Applying Pettigrew and Whipp's theory has been common in different sectors in the process of strategic changes. One of the prominent examples is the medical industry. Researchers have used Pettigrew and Whipp's dimensions of strategic change framework for the studies in health care organizations (a) to operationalize evidence-based practice, (b) to reduce hospital waiting times, and (c) to coordinate health and mental care (Klarare et al., 2020). For example, Stetler et al. (2007, 2009) used the Pettigrew and Whipp model to analyze the successful implementation and institutionalization of evidence-based practice in health care, focusing on the three primary dimensions.

A researcher can categorize the interview questions based on the dimensions, factors, or combination of both in the Pettigrew and Whipp dimensions of the strategic change framework. For an interview structure inspired by Pettigrew and Whipp's dimensions of the strategic change framework, researchers may categorize the interview questions into three categories: context, content, and process (Klarare et al., 2020; Stetler et al., 2007). Researchers can further use the dimensions, factors, or combination of both to transcribe the interviews. The researcher can initially code the interview transcript with pre-determined codes of context, content, and process dimensions to be broken later into more themes (Klarare et al., 2020).

Environmental Assessment

Environmental assessment is one of the essential sections of the strategic change framework. The study of different categories of the environment may result in a more detailed environmental assessment. In this study, the reviewed environments were regulatory, economic, and industrial, resulting in a comprehensive view of the current environment.

Regulatory Environment Assessment

The oil and gas industry is a naturally high-risk industry, requiring intensive regulations to address risks associated with drilling, production, processing, and distribution (Wanasinghe et al., 2020). Intensive exploitation of natural resources has been the cause of several environmental concerns (Alqahtani et al., 2019), which are present in the oil and gas industry, where the operations may be quite challenging in certain circumstances. The extreme environments in the oil and gas industry, such as deep waters, frigid regions, and undeveloped deserts, are the geographic challenges in the exploration and production of oil and gas (Chen et al., 2014). For example, offshore oil platforms are in need of constant monitoring in extreme weather, such as hurricanes and tsunamis, to spot any dangers (Zuo et al., 2021).

In the oil and gas industry, the challenges of obtaining oil and gas from both conventional and non-conventional resources have increased over time (Chen et al., 2014). The majority of easily reachable onshore and offshore oil and gas fields have declined because of production, requiring exploration and development of new fields located in extreme conditions, including but not limited to deserts, arctic zones, and deep-water (Shukla & Karki, 2016b). The increased challenges in extracting oil and gas from new hydrocarbon sources have been an addition to the complications in the oil and gas industry. The development of the oil and gas fields in extreme environments has been a reason for a higher cost of operations, as well as a higher risk to health, safety, and environment (HSE), and more demand for advanced technological innovations (Shukla & Karki, 2016b).

Though the operations in both onshore and offshore environments may be risky, the offshore environments may have some additional concerns. The concerns on the offshore installations are (a) atmosphere which could be explosive, toxic, and corrosive; (b) unsheltered maritime environment with insufficient protection against saltwater spray, direct sunlight, and the reflection of the sun from the sea surface; (c) heavy weather, such as wind, storm, rain, hail, and snow; (d) extreme ambient temperature and humidity; (e) constraint space; and (f) complicated logistics with people living on installations and the required emergency evacuations (Chen et al., 2014). The oil and gas companies should reduce costs in the mentioned extreme environment to remain competitive in the industry (Chen et al., 2014). In extreme offshore environments, the application of robots for monitoring and preventing risk is safer and more economical than human involvement (Zuo et al., 2021).

In the oil and gas industry, catastrophic incidents that happened in the past resulted in changes in the regulatory environment. An example of those high-impact catastrophic events is what happened in the Gulf of Mexico in 2010. The explosion of the Deepwater Horizon drilling rig on April 20, 2010 resulted in releasing of approximately 4 to 5 million barrels of crude oil into the Gulf of Mexico until September 19, 2010 (Allmon et al., 2022; Pinkston & Flemings, 2019; Rodgers et al., 2018; Serafin et al., 2019). After the Deepwater Horizon disaster, the researchers worked with the United States government to evaluate the U.S. regulatory regime for offshore accident prevention (Yang, 2018). As the outcome of the investigations, a site-specific approach is in place instead of the previous generic approach (Yang, 2018).

Economic Environment Assessment

Oil and gas have had a unique position among all energy sources. With urbanization, industrialization, and the growing world population, the global demand for fossil fuels, especially oil and gas, has increased (Shukla & Karki, 2016b). Oil and gas have some advantages over other energy sources. There is no equivalent substitute for oil and gas with an established infrastructure that can provide similar energy density and ease of transportation (Shukla & Karki, 2016a).

Recessions and downturns have not been rare. The downturns have affected various businesses worldwide in different time windows. To survive the downturn, business leaders have mainly selected the traditional approach. In response to the global recession, many companies lowered their costs by applying low-cost labor instead of focusing on increasing the added value of the performed job by the workers (Alcácer & Cruz-Machado, 2019). What previously worked may not be suitable for the existing economic environment. Since the circumstances have changed over time, companies have started evaluating other potential approaches. Companies are more interested in restoring their competitiveness through digital transformation (Alcácer & Cruz-Machado, 2019).

The oil and gas industry has gone through many instabilities in oil prices from 2014 onwards for up to a 70% cut (Lu et al., 2019a). The instability of oil prices has been costly to all stakeholders in the oil industry. Many companies in the oil and gas industry had difficulty maintaining their profitability and became candidates for being acquired by other companies (Lu et al., 2019a). The instabilities of oil prices have not only had effects on the companies. The oil price fluctuations generally have had impacts on the economic activities of countries (Bagirov & Mateus, 2019).

Fluctuations in oil prices may substantially impact the oil and gas industry. Lack of stability in oil prices, resulting in sharp increases or declines, has not been a rare episode in the oil and gas industry (Bagirov & Mateus, 2019). Supply and demand have an effect on oil and gas prices and precautionary motives (Caldara et al., 2019; Kilian, 2022; Kilian & Zhou, 2018; Lu et al., 2019a; Prest, 2018).

The oil and gas prices have had fluctuations over the past 40 years as a reaction to the forces of supply and demand (Baumeister & Kilian, 2016). Every fluctuation has happened for specific reasons. The variations were mainly because of (a) production shocks related to political events, new oil and gas discoveries, and technological advancements; (b) demand shocks related to global business cycles; and (c) demand shocks related to above-ground oil and gas inventories (Baumeister & Hamilton, 2019; Baumeister & Kilian, 2016). While there is consensus on reviewed factors influencing oil and gas prices, there is disagreement on the size of each factor on real oil and gas prices (Baumeister & Hamilton, 2019; Herrera & Rangaraju, 2019; Kilian & Zhou, 2018).

The shock occurrences are because of the gap between the expected price of oil and gas and the eventual price (Baumeister & Kilian, 2016). One example is the oil price reduction from $134 per barrel in 2008 to $39 per barrel in 2009 in eight months (Baumeister & Kilian, 2016). Another example is oil price reduction from $112 per barrel in 2014 to $47 per barrel in 2015 in only seven months (Baumeister & Kilian, 2016). The examples are indications of how extreme these fluctuations in the prices may be at times, resulting in severe interruptions in the supply chain. Therefore, it is logical to consider the supply chain disruption risk as a risk category.

The oil and gas price fluctuations have an intensive effect on the supply chain. Therefore, underestimating the risk of supply chain disruption may have severe consequences. A supply chain disruption risk is a combination of irregular events affecting the state of the supply chain (Kbah et al., 2020). The resilience of the companies in the oil and gas industry, in case of price instability, is dependent on the effectiveness of their risk management in supply chain disruption. Suitable mitigation strategies to handle the supply chain disruption risk are a strategic advantage for the companies (Kbah et al.,

2020). Supply chain management requires enhanced visibility in seeing what is happening, improved analytics in analyzing the change, and superior flexibility and agility in taking actions (Hofmann et al., 2019).

With higher oil prices, developing new oil and gas fields has mainly been the mechanism to increase oil production (Baumeister & Kilian, 2016). Nevertheless, in the US shale oil boom, the improved technologies in horizontal drilling and fracturing were the mechanism to increase oil production (Baumeister & Kilian, 2016; Stocker et al., 2018). The proof of flexibility and resilience of the US shale oil technology was at the oil price plunge in 2014 with about five times better response than conventional oil drilling (Stocker et al., 2018). The cost of shale oil drilling reduced over time because of better well designs resulting in shorter drilling and completion times with improved production rates (Stocker et al., 2018).

There are many reasons for the instabilities and fluctuations in oil and gas prices. The shale oil revolution in the United States has had an effect on oil supply and prices (Newell & Prest, 2019; Prest, 2018). Another example is the severe impact of the COVID-19 outbreak in early 2020 on economic environment deterioration in the oil and gas industry and many other industries. Nevertheless, considering the recency of the COVID-19 pandemic, peer-reviewed information was not available on the effects of the pandemic on different industries at the time of this study.

Industrial Environment Assessment

In 2011, Germany was the first to speak about Industry 4.0 for the manufacturing industry (Alcácer & Cruz-Machado, 2019; Dalenogare et al., 2018; Dev et al., 2020;

Mogos et al., 2019). In April 2013, Germany officially proposed the concept of Industry 4.0 (Lu et al., 2019a). To explore the scope of Industry 4.0, reviewing the industry 4.0 framework is beneficial. Table 3 is the strategic framework suggested by Germany for Industry 4.0 (Lu et al., 2019a).

Industry 4.0 is the fourth industrial revolution resulting in the digitalization era, interconnecting the different elements through a virtual environment (Alcácer & Cruz-Machado, 2019; Büchi et al., 2020). Industry 4.0 is compatible with the progress made in information technology. Industry 4.0 is the intelligence era, promoting industrial change through integrating industrialization and informatization (Dalenogare et al., 2018; Lu et al., 2019a).

The expectation from Industry 4.0 is to digitally transform people's lives by introducing new business models and ways of manufacturing (Alcácer & Cruz-Machado, 2019; Tortorella et al., 2020). As expected in any change process, resistance to change is inevitable. The aim of Industry 4.0 is to use advanced digitalization to improve operational productivity and operational efficiency (Alcácer & Cruz-Machado, 2019; Fatorachian & Kazemi, 2018; Fettermann et al., 2018). Through the application of Industry 4.0, the traditional industry will become interconnected by combining the virtual and physical worlds (Alcácer & Cruz-Machado, 2019; Fatorachian & Kazemi, 2018; Frank et al., 2019). Nevertheless, learning will be involved in the process, requiring patience and continuous improvement to achieve the expected outcome.

Table 3

Strategic Framework of Germany's Industry 4.0

One network	Cyber-physical system
Four themes	Smart factory
	Smart production
	Smart logistics
	Smart services
Three integrations	Vertical
	Horizontal
	End-to-end
Eight plans	Standardized reference framework
	Managing complex systems
	Industrial broadband foundation
	Safety and security
	Organization and planning of work
	Training and re-education
	Regulatory framework
	Resource utilization efficiency

Industry 4.0 will rapidly change and reshape conventional industrial processes,

enabled by ubiquitous internet access, machine-to-machine communications, and

advanced data analysis (Fatorachian & Kazemi, 2018; Pilloni, 2018; Toma & Popa,

2018). The creation of the Industry 4.0 concept was in Germany, but the idea became

quickly international. After Germany, some other countries such as China, the United

States, and Japan started their strategic plans for Industry 4.0 (Dalenogare et al., 2018; Lu

et al., 2019a; Mogos et al., 2019). The spread of Industry 4.0 did not stop in the

mentioned countries. More countries joined the list of Industry 4.0 adopters, including

France, the UK, South Korea, Japan, and Singapore (Liao et al., 2017). The focus of the

United States for Industry 4.0 has been on re-industrialization through big data, software,

and the internet, by merging the traditional networks and entities, reshaping

manufacturing through big data analytics, and connecting people, data, and machines in a global industrial network (Lu et al., 2019a).

Required Resources (Structure, Process, People)

Strategic change may be costly, requiring financial, human, and other resources (Wiedner et al., 2017). Some strategic changes may not be successful. Insufficient resources could be the cause of failure when implementing strategic changes (Wiedner et al., 2017). Strategic changes are not only about the addition of resources. In the process of a strategic change, revaluation and redistribution of resources could be common (Wiedner et al., 2017). For a successful strategic change, the change agents should remain engaged in assessing and adjusting the change process as required (Uvhagen et al., 2018). The necessary resources are a combination of structure, process, and people.

One of the resources required for Industry 4.0 implementation is structure. The reference model for Industry 4.0, as a guide for technology implementation, is a 3D model creating a structured framework with a shared language (Alcácer & Cruz-Machado, 2019). The three axes of the 3D model for Industry 4.0 are (a) facilities and product lifecycle including instance and type; (b) hierarchical level of the enterprise including product level, field device level, control device level, station level, work centers level, the enterprise level, and the connected world level; and (c) functional layers including asset layer, integration layer, communication layer, information layer, functional layer, and business layer (Alcácer & Cruz-Machado, 2019). The nine critical technologies of Industry 4.0 are (a) Internet of Things (IoT), (b) big data, (c) cybersecurity, (d) cloud computing, (e) simulation or digital twin, (f) additive manufacturing or 3D printing, (g) augmented reality, (h) system integration, and (i) intelligent robotics (Alcácer & Cruz-Machado, 2019; Lu et al., 2019a; Pilloni, 2018).

The first key technology for Industry 4.0 is IoT. By applying IoT, people and things can connect through any network regardless of time and place (Sezer et al., 2018). The connection of everything to the internet may happen at one point by IoT (Cedeño et al., 2018; Hammoudi et al., 2018; Qi & Tao, 2018; Tao et al., 2018). IoT is an enabler for creating interconnectivity of the system parts and reducing the chances of working in silos. The application of IoT can result in the conversion of the world into an intelligent world, adapting to a human's lifestyle (Hammoudi et al., 2018).

In the industrial environment, the industrial Internet of Things (IIoT) is a more reliable connection between the industrial component and the internet (Alcácer & Cruz-Machado, 2019; Cedeño et al., 2018). Reliability is an assurance of the uptime and the security of the system. For reliable performance in the smart world, challenges like architecture, privacy, security, openness, standardization, mobility, scalability, energy conservation for extended longevity, and quality of services exist (Hammoudi et al., 2018).

The second key technology for Industry 4.0 is big data. After connecting things to the internet under the IoT concept, a large volume of structured, semistructured, and unstructured data will be available, called big data (Qi & Tao, 2018; Tao et al., 2018). Big data is complex data at large volumes, with high velocity captured, stored, and managed by advanced techniques (Alcácer & Cruz-Machado, 2019). The utilization of data to add value to the process is the key. While data collection and storage create big data, the value remains in meaningful data analysis (Alcácer & Cruz-Machado, 2019).

Making sense of big data could be lengthy and costly (Alcácer & Cruz-Machado, 2019).

Big data is characterized mainly by the three V's of volume, variety, and velocity

(Alcácer & Cruz-Machado, 2019).

The third key technology for Industry 4.0 is cybersecurity. A significant increase

in data volumes is the outcome of Industry 4.0, requiring data protection and

cybersecurity more than before (Fataliyev & Mehdiyev, 2020). With IoT as an

interconnection of people and things through a network, an additional complexity in

security and vulnerability is inevitable (Dutta et al., 2020). There has been an evolution

of internet threats into well-organized cybercrime (Skopik et al., 2016). The oil and gas

industry has not been an exception. Considering the criticality of the oil and gas industry,

and given that remote controlling of these critical systems is sometimes the case,

recognizing and mitigating such attacks are essential (Stergiopoulos et al., 2020). The

attack detection mechanism must match the increased complexity. Attack detection

within individual organizations may not be sufficient anymore, requiring cross-

organizational information sharing for a thorough understanding of large-scale cyber-

attack threats (Skopik et al., 2016).

A combination of cyber and physical components is a cyber-physical system

(CPS) (Alqahtani et al., 2019; Delicato et al., 2020; Fatorachian & Kazemi, 2018; Huang

et al., 2018). The resilience of the CPS against cyber-attacks and malicious activities is a

critical topic referred to as cybersecurity. The critical infrastructures are CPS. Enhancing

the resilience against cyber-attacks on critical infrastructures through prevention,

mitigation, and restoration is crucial (Huang et al., 2018).

Cloud computing is the fourth key technology for Industry 4.0. Cloud computing is one of the techniques suitable for companies considering outsourcing their IT resources. Adopting cloud computing will be dependent on factors such as technology readiness, management support, relative advantage, security, privacy, and Costs (Nguyen et al., 2021). The benefits of cloud computing are (a) removing the cost of IT infrastructure in the organization, (b) providing a flexible pool of resources, and (c) providing broad, reliable network access (Alcácer & Cruz-Machado, 2019). Cloud computing has robust computing power, using various models and algorithms to organize, analyze, and mine the big data to provide meaningful knowledge (Qi & Tao, 2018).

Everything in the cloud is a service in a layered system with access to the public, private, hybrid, and community (Alcácer & Cruz-Machado, 2019). The frequent increase in cloud usage is one reason for an additional risk introduced to the systems (Oliveira et al., 2019). The layers of services in the cloud are (a) infrastructure as a service (IaaS), including virtual servers, networks, operating systems, and applications; (b) platform as a service (PaaS), providing users the access to build, run, and deploy their applications in the remote IT platform; (c) software as a service (SaaS) with applications in a cloud infrastructure available for users; and (d) everything as a service (XaaS) including IaaS, PaaS, and SaaS (Alcácer & Cruz-Machado, 2019).

The fifth key technology for Industry 4.0 is simulation or digital twin. Simulation is the imitation of an existing system to run some experiments for validation of products, processes, or system configurations (Alcácer & Cruz-Machado, 2019). Based on what the authors claimed, different simulations were available such as static, dynamic, offline, and online. The authors identified selecting a suitable simulation type as a multiparameter decision. Offline simulations are ideal for analyzing what-if scenarios (Alcácer & Cruz-Machado, 2019). Online simulation is a real-time simulation running on a computer at the same rate as the physical system facilitated by IoT (Cedeño et al., 2018). Digital Twin is another concept in simulation with a critical role in Industry 4.0 (Alcácer & Cruz-Machado, 2019).

The sixth key technology for Industry 4.0 is additive manufacturing or 3D printing. Additive manufacturing is a disruptive technology for creating objects from 3D data in a layer-upon-layer format (Basak et al., 2022; Jiang et al., 2017; Kleer & Piller, 2019). Additive manufacturing has other naming conventions such as rapid prototyping, solid freeform manufacturing, and digital manufacturing (Alcácer & Cruz-Machado, 2019). Additive manufacturing is a highly transformative technology, restricted to a niche market until recently, but the cost of this technology has significantly reduced in the past few years (Rayna & Striukova, 2021).

Augmented reality is the seventh key technology for Industry 4.0. Augmented reality is to augment the real world with virtual things (Palmarini et al., 2018). In other words, in augmented reality, a real-world physical environment exists alongside some virtual elements (Fraga-Lamas et al., 2018). Augmented reality has applications in different sectors like education, healthcare, engineering, and gaming (Xiong et al., 2021). The augmented reality system has hardware, development software, and a visualization method. The main objective of augmented reality technology is to improve human performance through powerful tools such as Human-Machine Interface (Alcácer & Cruz-Machado, 2019).

The elements of augmented reality are (a) camera, (b) display, (c) processing unit, and (d) activating components such as sensors, GPS positions, and images (Alcácer & Cruz-Machado, 2019). Visualization for the user of augmented reality happens through devices: (a) worn on the user's head called head-mounted, (b) held in the user's hand called handheld, or (c) placed in the user's environment called spatial (Danielsson et al., 2020). The application of augmented reality in the industrial field is the industrial augmented reality, supporting the industrial processes (Fraga-Lamas et al., 2018). Maintenance and diagnostic areas are relevant fields for augmented reality, enhancing the execution of tasks and decision-making (Alcácer & Cruz-Machado, 2019).

The eighth key technology for Industry 4.0 is system integration. The three approaches for system integration in Industry 4.0 are horizontal, vertical, and end-to-end, affecting the real-time data sharing methodology (Alcácer & Cruz-Machado, 2019; Salkin et al., 2018). The horizontal approach is inter-company, and the vertical approach is intra-company (Alcácer & Cruz-Machado, 2019).

The ninth key technology for Industry 4.0 is intelligent robotics. The different levels of automation for robotics are (a) fully automatic with no human intervention, (b) semi-automatic with varying degrees of human interaction, and (c) manual with the human decision-makers within the control loop (Chen et al., 2014). To make automation and robotics a success in the oil and gas industry, the right level of automation with the integration of humans, technology, and automation will be critical (Chen et al., 2014).

Robotics is a sign of advancement in engineering for the adapting industry (Hajjaj & Khalid, 2018). The authors claimed robots performed labor-intensive and unsafe tasks for humans in different environments, including difficult-to-reach, impossible-to-reach for humans, or unsafe-to-reach because of limitations such as size, pressure, temperature, toxin, and more. The authors claimed the benefits of robotics were security and safety improvement and cost-saving through reducing reoccurring expenses, saving time, and improving efficiency. The robots are either autonomous, semi-autonomous, or manual through a controller (Hajjaj & Khalid, 2018).

In different industries addressing a significant gap in the availability and cost of various resources such as structure, process, and people may be inevitable for onboarding Industry 4.0. While many industries may be interested in adopting Industry 4.0, the existence of a framework for implementation of Industry 4.0 may be an area of improvement (Zheng et al., 2018). Upgrade to Industry 4.0 can happen in stages to avoid high initial costs and complications of the process. Identifying the priorities in the related industry for advanced digitalization will be critical to the success of the process (Alexandrova & Prudsky, 2019).

Linking Strategic and Operational Changes

The maturity of advanced digitalization is not the same in different industries. Some industries have high safety concerns, making them suitable candidates for advanced digitalization. The nuclear industry, as well as the petrochemical industry, are two examples of industries with critical safety concerns (Hajjaj & Khalid, 2018).

The maturity of advanced digitalization varies even in different parts of the same industry. Advanced digitalization is more advanced in some areas of the oil and gas industry, such as maintenance and inspection, to improve safety, quality, and reliability, while reducing cost. Different examples of such applications are available. Frequent maintenance and inspection of the pipe to assure reliable working conditions are essential, considering the criticality of the pipelines in the oil and gas industry with high technology design applied to unique material (Hajjaj & Khalid, 2018). The breakage of a pipeline may result in hydrocarbon loss and an environmental disaster, which will be even more critical in the marine environment (Li et al., 2017).

For digital transformation in every industry, understanding priorities, opportunities, and risks are non-negotiable (Alexandrova & Prudsky, 2019). Setting the right priorities for advanced digitalization in any sector may result in substantially positive outcomes for that industry. An example of setting priorities could be starting with advanced digitalization of costly operations. Inspecting, cleaning, and maintaining pipelines and tanks could be expensive in the oil and gas industry. Considering how costly and frequent the inspection, cleaning, and maintenance of pipelines and tanks could be, the application of robots could be of value (Hajjaj & Khalid, 2018). The right type of advanced digitalization can be an undeniable success factor. Therefore, managers should consider selecting a suitable digitalization as a critical step. For inspection of the pipes, as an example, three types of robots exist (a) caterpillar type, (b) mobile type, and (c) wheeled type, each with its advantages and disadvantages (Hajjaj & Khalid, 2018).

The potential benefits of robotics application as a part of advanced digitalization are (a) providing a less error-prone environment with higher reliability and more result consistency, (b) increasing production efficiency, (c) improving the safety of the operations, (d) reducing the cost of remote offshore operations through remotely controlled unstaffed offshore oil and gas facilities (Chen et al., 2014; Shukla & Karki, 2016b). The first applications of robotics in the oil and gas industry have been deep water and ultra-deepwater (Rémouit et al., 2018). The application of robotics and automation for specific operations, such as inspection, maintenance, and repair in the offshore oil and gas industry, have resulted in safer and more efficient operations (Chen et al., 2014). Some of the same technologies in offshore oil and gas exploitations have also been relevant to the offshore renewable energy sector (Rémouit et al., 2018).

One of the safest and most economical means of hydrocarbon fluid transportation is pipelines that extend millions of miles worldwide (Adegboye et al., 2019). The leakage detection technologies are critical, considering that the consequences of leakage in the pipeline networks may be environmental disasters, casualties, and financial losses (Adegboye et al., 2019). Pipeline leakage detection methods are (a) exterior, including acoustic sensing, fiber optic sensing, vapor sampling, infrared thermography, and ground penetration radar; (b) visual or biological, including the use of trained dogs, experienced personnel, smart pigging, or drones; and (c) interior or computational including continuous monitoring of the fluid inside the pipeline for pressure, temperature, flow rate, density, and other characteristics used in different algorithms for leakage detection (Adegboye et al., 2019; Chen et al., 2014).

Potential Benefits of Advanced Digitalization

The expectation from Industry 4.0, like any other change, is to add value. The potential benefits of Industry 4.0 are available in different scholarly pieces of literature, with some examples provided in this section. The advantage of Industry 4.0 is to create smart manufacturing capable of assisting in creative problem solving and decision making with the outcome of intelligent products (Alcácer & Cruz-Machado, 2019). One impact of Industry 4.0 could be using advanced digitalization to perform tedious, repetitive, or physically demanding jobs (Alcácer & Cruz-Machado, 2019; Dachs et al., 2019).

Besides creating smart processes and products and freeing humans for further focus on non-repetitive tasks, Industry 4.0 could result in other benefits. Considering the change in the customers' requirements, agility, efficiency, responsiveness, product quality, and regulatory compliance are even more essential (Fatorachian & Kazemi, 2018). Through the application of Industry 4.0, the firms may have better control at a reduced cost of coordination over the network of employees, suppliers, and customers in geographically dispersed locations (Dachs et al., 2019). The potential benefit of Industry 4.0 is not only in cost reduction. Applying technologies in Industry 4.0 could result in improved reliability, increased performance, and reduced wasted resources, minimizing carbon emissions and production expenses (Lafferty, 2019; Liu & De Giovanni, 2019). Therefore, the benefit of possible environmental protection from Industry 4.0 is valuable.

Another benefit of Industry 4.0 may be in increasing the lifecycle of the products. Many manufacturing companies have adopted end-of-life strategies to reduce waste through environmental-friendly approaches, which may result in cost-saving and extension of the product lifecycle (Garrido-Hidalgo et al., 2019). The focus of the circular economy and reverse logistics is on improving the economic and environmental aspects of manufacturing (Dev et al., 2020).

Potential Challenges of Advanced Digitalization

One of the common concerns related to advanced digitalization is the fear of robots taking over human jobs (Acemoglu & Restrepo, 2018; Jarrahi, 2018; Khan, 2018; Nica, 2018). With the concern of robots replacing humans in the workplace, resistance against advanced digitalization may increase. Some researchers expressed concern that the impact of advanced digitalization should not be eliminating jobs but rather changing what people are doing for better business results (Barro & Davenport, 2019; Jarrahi, 2018). Other researchers have expected Industry 4.0 to introduce more collaborative flexibility to the production system (Alcácer & Cruz-Machado, 2019). After adopting Industry 4.0, redefining job roles into three categories human-specific, machine-specific, and shared tasks, will be inevitable (Ansari et al., 2018).

Digitalization may have social implications by altering inter-organizational and intra-organizational relationships (Ghobakhloo & Fathi, 2019). There may be a risk of unemployment in the low-skilled workforce in the digitalized environment, in addition to the risk of data security and privacy (Ghobakhloo & Fathi, 2019). To cope with the challenges of industry 4.0, preparedness for a possible change in the skill requirements is logical. The technology-savvy universities may have a critical role in preparing flexible and independent graduates capable of adopting their skillsets in the industry 4.0 era (Nguyen, 2018).

The success of Industry 4.0 will be dependent on appropriate strategic implementation. The steering of the advanced digitalization process towards safeguarding economic, social, and environmental sustainability should be the commitment of companies and industries (Ghobakhloo & Fathi, 2019). Industry 4.0 is about creating new opportunities alongside new vulnerabilities (Büchi et al., 2020). For successful implementation of Industry 4.0, resulting in a positive impact on business and society, management of the vulnerabilities will be critical (Büchi et al., 2020).

Protecting the valuable data created through Industry 4.0 and making the data only available to authorized users is critical (Alcácer & Cruz-Machado, 2019). While different industries are in agreement with global digitalization as the way forward, many companies could be ignorant of the potential threats of advanced digitalization to their business (Peskova et al., 2019). Some applications of artificial intelligence are in different industries, such as healthcare, transportation, and the justice system (Casares, 2018). Implementation of advanced digitalization is more challenging in the offshore environment because of the complexity and the remote nature of offshore installations, with a high risk of corrosion, explosion, and radiation, in harsh environments with extreme temperature and high humidity (Chen et al., 2014).

Leading Advanced Digitalization Change

Implementing a change process to adopt Industry 4.0 may not be easy for different companies. The interpretation of executive management from the concept of Industry 4.0, its driving forces, and its barriers will be critical to the success of the process (Horváth & Szabó, 2019). The researchers have performed studies to identify the driving forces and obstacles of Industry 4.0. Referring to Horváth and Szabó (2019), the main driving force for the management in adopting industry 4.0 is the ability to access real-time performance measurements alongside the production factors. Defining the strategic roadmap by the executive management of a firm for managing the advanced digitization process aligned with the mandate of Industry 4.0 may benefit the digital transformation process (Ghobakhloo & Fathi, 2019).

Like any other change process, resistance against change is inevitable in adopting Industry 4.0. Developing an Industry 4.0 strategy is challenging (Bakon et al., 2022). The Executive management should be ready to address potential technological, organizational, and management challenges through the change process (Ghobakhloo & Fathi, 2019; Horváth & Szabó, 2019). A detailed implementation plan should be a resolution to the mentioned issue. The organizational resistance could be from middle managers and employees (Horváth & Szabó, 2019). Industry 4.0 has been the main change in the human-machine relationship to human-machine cooperation, as the human worker receives assistance from the machine through interacting and exchanging information (Ansari et al., 2018).

While the confrontation of the organization is not surprising, the right strategy to lower the mentioned resistance should be in place. If the executive managers fail to address the resistance efficiently, introducing Industry 4.0 technologies may get complicated (Horváth & Szabó, 2019). Failure in the adoption of Industry 4.0 may happen for different reasons. Two significant risks in adopting Industry 4.0 are lack of expertise and a short-term strategy mindset (Galli, 2018; Moeuf et al., 2020). Therefore, executive management should not underestimate the importance of adequate training and a long-term strategy. Strategic changes are often dynamic ones requiring a clear vision understood by the organization and backed up by well-defined targets (Eriksson & Fundin, 2018). Having the right strategy is essential in a strategic change, while effective communication of that strategy to the organization is as essential (Eriksson & Fundin, 2018; Galli, 2018). Performance measurement during the implementation of a strategic change may result in creating a track record of the effectiveness of that change (Abernethy et al., 2021).

Modern economic development is closely interrelated to digital technologies (Peskova et al., 2019). Some managers in oil companies have partially recognized the potential value of advanced digitalization. Some scientists, describing the digital technology management in oil companies' current practice, point to the lack of rapid digitalization processes implementation. According to experts, digital transformation could have an effect on all areas of business (e.g., current, investment, and financial) while improving the business environment of companies (Peskova et al., 2019). The companies should be open to creating, retaining, and transferring the knowledge related to Industry 4.0 technologies within their organizations to remain competitive (Tortorella et al., 2020). With the complexity resulting from Industry 4.0 in the workspace, education and training for new skills and competencies may become inevitable (Lupicka & Grzybowska, 2018).

The adoption of Industry 4.0 may be related to the company's size. Based on the studies, multinational enterprises have higher driving forces in implementing industry 4.0 (Horváth & Szabó, 2019). In the transition to Industry 4.0, organizational integration of many IT technologies at different levels of the companies will be required (Ghobakhloo & Fathi, 2019). While multinational enterprises may have a potential advantage over smaller companies, no red line exists for smaller companies adopting Industry 4.0. Smaller companies may still be able to onboard Industry 4.0 (Horváth & Szabó, 2019). Industry 4.0 transition in small companies may happen in stages, introducing digitization to certain operations areas by priority (Ghobakhloo & Fathi, 2019).

There are different examples of advanced digitalization activities supported by oil companies. The gradual shift of the oil and gas industry towards advanced digitalization has been noticeable (Lu et al., 2019a; Lu et al., 2019b). The examples of the mentioned shift are available. Many exploration and production operations in Total, a major energy player, are happening in challenging conditions such as extreme hot or cold climates in remote, isolated locations ("ARGOS Challenge," 2017).

Considering the value that the autonomous robots may add to the safety of the onshore and offshore operations, Total partnered with the French National Research Agency (ANR) in 2013 to launch ARGOS Challenge ("ARGOS Challenge," 2017). ARGOS is the Autonomous Robot for Gas and Oil Sites, fulfilling the objective of reaching a massive deployment of autonomous robots in industrial facilities (Merriaux et al., 2018). Fit-for-purpose design of robots could add the highest value to the performed activities by robots. Different examples of fit-for-purpose designs are available. For instance, for patrolling the oil and gas platforms, the robots should be able to travel safely on the platform between the floors, bypass different obstacles, climb the stairs, and detect the emergency alarms (Merriaux et al., 2018).

The oil and gas platforms could be dangerous for humans considering different operations taking place on them. Therefore, the preference is to keep people to the minimum whenever possible. Patrolling oil and gas infrastructures using autonomous robots could result in increased safety standards by operating without any humans on the platforms in some cases (Merriaux et al., 2018). In accidents, using robots could be an enabler in accessing locations that could be dangerous for humans. On many occasions, robots could have access to places humans may not be able to access for various reasons. During a fire, hydrocarbon leaks, and explosions, using robots to deal with the situation is worthwhile without risking human life (Merriaux et al., 2018).

There are other examples of oil and gas companies that embarked on advanced digitalization. For instance, the following oil companies in Russia are active in advanced digitalization: Transneft, Gazprom Neft, and the LUKOIL group of companies (Alexandrova & Prudsky, 2019). Also, in many large oil and gas companies, the management has focused on blockchain technology to significantly improve efficiency and data security (Lu et al., 2019b).

Overall Coherence of Advanced Digitalization

Advanced digitalization may become an integral part of the oil and gas industry by providing logical and consistent outcomes. Based on the available literature, there are different examples of the possible coherence of advanced digitalization with oil and gas applications. According to Toma and Popa (2018), Industry 4.0 concepts are relevant to oil and gas like other industries. The authors also claimed that in the assurance of a safe cybersecurity environment, using the security best practices should become a critical requirement in every sector, including the oil and gas industry.

Successful change should be sustainable. Industry 4.0 is happening, and it is wise for organizations to gain a competitive advantage by applying the requirements of the changing environment (Dhanpat et al., 2020). A short-lasting change is a waste of resources. Advanced digitalization will have an effect on the employees and HR operations (Liboni et al., 2019). For sustainability, the employees should shift their capacities to the requirement of transformed workspaces with Industry 4.0 (Rana & Sharma, 2019). A sustainable economy may result in the promotion of global economic competitiveness through the intelligent use of resources and the creation of new job opportunities (Naudé, 2018). Adopting new employee skills and competencies is inevitable in Industry 4.0 (Lupicka & Grzybowska, 2018).

Customizing advanced digitalization solutions for the needs of each company is of critical importance. Transition to Industry 4.0 for different companies should be proportional to their organizational, operational, and technical particularities (Ghobakhloo & Fathi, 2019). When digitalization is fit for purpose based on the priorities, the companies will have more benefits. In adopting Industry 4.0, the managers should prioritize the company's core strategies for superior competitiveness (Ghobakhloo & Fathi, 2019). What works for one company may not be the best solution for another company.

Transition

Section 1 of this study introduced the business problem that some leaders in the oil and gas industry lacked successful strategies to implement advanced digitalization.

Section 1 had a thorough review of the background of the problem and the academic literature, analyzing the existing body of knowledge to establish the basis for the study. The structure of the academic literature review is in reference to Pettigrew and Whipp's dimensions of strategic change theory.

Section 2 is a reiteration of the purpose statement, followed by the role of the researcher and the participants. Section 2 includes the selected research method and design with the related justifications for choosing the method and design. Moreover, Section 2 is a review of ethical research, data collection instruments and techniques, data organization techniques, data analysis, and reliability and validity of the information.

Section 3 is a review of the study's detailed findings pertinent to the business problem. In addition to the study's results, the researcher's recommendation for future research is a part of Section 3. Another significant element in Section 3 is the discussion of the possible social changes this doctoral study could have.

Section 2: The Project

In Section 1, the main elements were the background to the business problem, the problem statement, the research purpose, the nature of the study, the research question, interview questions, the conceptual framework, operational definitions, significance of study, assumptions, limitations, and delimitations. The analysis of the available scholarly literature related to advanced digitalization was a significant element of Section 1. In Section 2, the main components are a reiteration of the purpose statement, identification of the researcher's role, the participants, the research method and design, population and sampling, ethical research, data collection instruments and techniques, data organization techniques, data analysis, and reliability and validity.

Purpose Statement

The purpose of this qualitative multiple case study was to explore successful strategies some leaders in the oil and gas industry used to implement advanced digitalization. The target population was a minimum of four leaders in at least two companies, preferably one oil service company and one oil company in North America, who successfully created and utilized advanced digitalization in the oil and gas industry. This study may lead to a positive social change by encouraging advanced digitalization in the oil and gas industry, resulting in the creation of more job opportunities for the local workers and companies, reducing job stress, and improving the domestic economy and level of prosperity.

Role of the Researcher

The researcher is critical in a qualitative study (Fusch & Ness, 2015). The researcher is responsible for the type of research question, the control mechanisms, and the focus on either contemporary or historical events for identifying the research design (Yin, 2018). The researcher is also embedded in the research as a data collection instrument (Rutberg & Bouikidis, 2018). In my doctoral research, I was the primary instrument for data collection. I ensured briefing the participants on the purpose of the study, the interview questions, the data collection process through interviews, and the data analysis process. Having worked in the oil industry all my career, I knew the study participants directly or indirectly. The participants in my interviews were the senior leaders in advanced digitalization. As an oil industry leader for almost two decades, I was familiar with the challenges in the mentioned sector. Nevertheless, I was committed to keeping an open mind throughout the data collection and analysis to minimize bias.

The researcher must maintain high ethical standards in research. To protect human subjects participating in the research, the National Commission for the Protection of Human Subjects of Biomedical and Behavioral Research (1979) has the *Belmont Report* summarizing the required principles and procedures—respect participants, limit the risk for the participants, and ensure justice through the application of consent forms (Brakewood & Poldrack, 2013; Friesen et al., 2017). I was committed to adhering to the three core principles identified in the *Belmont Report* throughout my doctoral research. As the researcher, I ensured the participants were aware of their role in the research process. I also respected the right of the participants to participate in the research freely based on their choice. I was cautious of the data confidentiality and only used the data for research purposes. I kept the identity of the participants and their related companies confidential. I treated the participants with respect and justice.

Further, a biased approach could have a negative effect on a study's validity and reliability. Therefore, I strived to reduce bias by interpreting the collected data for the investigated phenomenon based on the participants' opinions instead of my viewpoint. I ensured advanced preparation through having an interview protocol (a) to stay focused on addressing identified relevant concepts, (b) to be empowered with a sense of control, (c) to remain connected analytically by translating research questions into the conversation, and (d) to be enabled to continue the discussion in challenging conditions (Arsel, 2017).

Participants

The study participants must have in-depth information to provide productive responses to the research questions (Saunders & Townsend, 2016). The study participants must also be knowledgeable and experienced in the phenomenon under exploration (Patton, 2015). In my doctoral research, the study participants were supposed to be at least four advanced digitalization leaders in the oil and gas industry—preferably two from an oil service company and two from an oil company. The selected leaders had to have involvement in successfully implementing advanced digitalization in their respective companies. During the data collection phase, I only conducted interviews with the leaders of two oil service companies. Even though I had invited the oil companies' potential participants for the interviews, they did not participate due to data tightness and information-sharing limitations in their companies.

In proper research, establishing trust with participants is crucial (Celestina et al., 2018). In my research, the participants were encouraged to trust because of the shared interest we had in the industry. I accessed the participants through my working

relationship with them. I called the selected participants to provide them with some

background information on what I had planned to do and to request their participation if

they considered it appropriate. Then, I emailed the participants an invitation to participate

in my study. Upon participants' acceptance of the invitation, I emailed a letter of

voluntary cooperation to the advanced digitalization leaders that they signed and returned

to me. I also ensured the improvement of existing relationships by being open and

transparent, briefing the participants on the purpose and guidelines of the study.

Research Method and Design

Research Method

Researchers may use three methodologies in conducting their research:

qualitative, quantitative, and mixed (Yilmaz, 2013). For this study, I selected the

qualitative research method based on the focus of my doctoral study on an exploratory

concept. Advanced digitalization in the oil industry is a recent phenomenon to be studied

in an exploratory manner.

The qualitative method is suitable for a broad context of a business problem,

analyzing the data from direct fieldwork observations (Antwi & Hamza, 2015). Data

collection is often done through in-depth, open-ended interviews and written documents,

providing flexibility in interactions between the researcher and the study participants

(Antwi & Hamza, 2015; Marshall & Rossman, 2016; Yin, 2018). Therefore, the

qualitative method applies to exploratory research.

The quantitative method is suitable for defining the relationship between selected variables through the analysis of numerical data utilizing statistical techniques (Cronin, 2014). The quantitative method is formal, objective, and systematic, with many participants representing a population (Yilmaz, 2013). In the quantitative method, the researcher often tests a hypothesis and focuses on closed-ended questions (Marshall & Rossman, 2016; Ridder, 2017). Considering advanced digitalization is at an early stage of development, as well as restrictions on the confidentiality of data, the quantitative data was not available to me. I performed interviews with open-ended questions without testing any hypotheses Therefore, the quantitative method was not the right choice for exploratory research. The mixed-method approach is a combination of qualitative and quantitative methods, producing comprehensive outcomes with more extensive information (Marshall & Rossman, 2016; McKim, 2017). Consequently, the qualitative method was the right choice for my research study. With a qualitative method, I gained insights into the strategies currently applied for the integration and advanced digitalization of services in the oil industry through interviews and qualitative analytical procedures.

Research Design

For selecting a research design, the researcher considers the type of research question, the control mechanisms, and the focus on either contemporary or historical events (Yin, 2018). The qualitative research designs include phenomenology, narrative, ethnography, and case study. After studying the application of available designs, I concluded the use of the case study was the right approach for my doctoral research on implementing advanced digitalization in the oil industry.

Phenomenology is a description of humans' experience with a particular phenomenon while setting aside bias in the process (Katsirikou & Lin, 2017; Marshall & Rossman, 2016). Phenomenology was not the right approach, as my focus was not on humans' experience regarding the advanced digitalization phenomenon. Narrative design is a description of an individual's story from their own life experience (Marshall & Rossman, 2016). The narrative design was not the right design because of the recency of advanced digitalization in the oil industry. Finally, ethnography is the direct observation of the study participants going through an experience in their environment (Ingold, 2014). My research topic was about advanced digitalization strategies, not the experience of people with advanced digitalization; therefore, ethnography was not a relevant design.

The case study design was the best approach for advanced digitalization in the oil and gas industry as a recent phenomenon in its infancy. In a case study, the researcher investigates a contemporary phenomenon in a real-life context with an in-depth, descriptive, and exploratory analysis of a person, group, events, decisions, periods, policies, institutions, or other systems (Ridder, 2017; Yin, 2018). The case study is applicable to the experiences in different situations with either typical or rare conditions (Connelly, 2014). Specifically, the multiple case study is suitable for researchers to explore details and perspectives concerning a specific situation replicated in more than a single case, offering a more reliable outcome (Yin, 2018).

Considering the case study as the right approach for my doctoral research, I required the application of triangulation. The focus of triangulation is on the process and methods of data collection (Yin, 2018). I conducted interviews with advanced digitalization leaders in two oil service companies, with no success interviewing anyone

from an oil company. Investigating a research topic is possible through contextualizing

the same phenomenon experienced by others (Bevan, 2014). Data saturation in

qualitative studies is when no new data, themes, or codings emerge, allowing the study to

replicate (Fusch & Ness, 2015). I ensured the data saturation in my doctoral study

through the lack of emergence of any new data, theme, and coding during the data

analysis process of my research.

Population and Sampling

The scope of the study defines the population. The sample size the researchers

select aligns with the research questions and the purpose statement (Khan, 2014). In my

research, I applied a multiple case study on implementing advanced digitalization in the

oil and gas industry. In multiple case studies, the population is everyone meeting the

participant criteria in various companies.

I interviewed seven advanced digitalization leaders from two oil service

companies, with no success in interviewing anyone from an oil company. The oil

companies are tightly limited in data sharing. Consequently, the potential participants

from the oil companies could not attend the interviews, even though I had provided them

with the invitations. Although advanced digitalization in the oil industry may not be fully

commercialized, the oil service companies are creating automated solutions to be used by

some oil companies. There is a close collaboration between oil service companies and oil

companies in developing and implementing advanced digitalization solutions. This close

collaboration has given oil service companies an excellent understanding of the expectations and requirements of the oil companies in implementing advanced digitalization. I interviewed three managers from one oil service company and four from another oil service company involved in the creation of advanced digitalization. In the interviews, I asked the oil service company participants to answer the interview questions from the perspectives of an oil service company as well as an oil company, given their close collaboration and understanding. With this approach, there may be some valuable findings for the oil companies as well as the oil service companies in this study.

Through purposeful data collection, the chance of reaching data saturation is higher (Palinkas et al., 2015); thus, the sampling strategy I selected was purposive. I chose participants based on the selection criteria of being a manager in charge of advanced digitalization in an oil company or an oil service company. My access to the participants was through professional relationships in my job in the oil industry. I provided the participants with a consent form to sign before holding the interviews. At the same time, I protected their identity by not sharing the organizations' and participants' names.

As the primary data collection instrument, I interviewed participants to obtain data using a set of semistructured interview questions (see Appendix A) in a one-on-one interview setting, on a video or phone call, voice recording the interviews with the permission of the participants. The interview was private, and the participants did not feel uncomfortable having other employees see them in this setting. I followed the interview protocol provided in Appendix B. I will keep the record of interviews secured for 5 years after the interview conduction. After that, I will delete the voice-recorded interviews and electronic documents. I will also destroy any paper copies.

The accuracy and validity of a qualitative study are through ensuring data saturation in qualitative research. There is no direct correlation between the sample size and data saturation in qualitative research. The critical characteristics of reaching data saturation are to have high-quality, in-depth data with no further emergence of any new data, themes, or coding, providing the ability to replicate the study (Fusch & Ness, 2015). Reaching data saturation is related to the study design. Through purposive sampling, the researcher approaches study participants with the best insight into the case (Palinkas et al., 2015). Additionally, the direct connection between method triangulation and data saturation has been identified (Fusch & Ness, 2015). Therefore, through accessing the right participants and applying triangulation, the researcher can reach data saturation with a smaller sample size.

I was confident in reaching data saturation with my selected sample size. I used purposive sampling along with data triangulation to facilitate data saturation. I still confirmed reaching data saturation in action after performing the interviews. I had planned to run a minimum of four interviews with the possibility of extending to more interviews or re-interviewing the same participants if reaching data saturation was not evident. I performed seven interviews, which resulted in apparent data saturation.

Ethical Research

The researcher's mission is to generate knowledge through a research process following ethical standards and principles (Chiumento et al., 2017; Le Roux, 2016). Ethical research is about respecting the study's participants by eliminating potential harm and maximizing benefits while practicing justice towards the individuals' societal levels (Yip et al., 2016). The researcher is responsible for protecting the privacy and confidentiality of the company's information and participants' information by utilizing federal and ethical standards. Fletcher (2017) has emphasized researchers' responsibility in the assurance of ethical research by considering participants' well-being in collecting data fulfilling the purpose of the study before considering any self-interest.

The researcher should follow the parameters established by the study's ethical review committee (Zhang, 2017). The approval of the plan from an institutional review board is a requirement for the initiation of the research (Yin, 2018). In this study, I ensured adherence to Walden's University ethical guidelines and directives of the Internal Review Board (IRB). As one of the requirements, I obtained formal consent, including a confidentiality agreement from the potential participants, by submitting a letter describing the research topic and objective before the interview process. The participants had the right to withdraw from the study by notifying me.

The researcher must ensure ethical capturing, protecting, and reporting of the information collected in the research process. In this study, the participant selection, the data collection, and the data storage reflected IRB standards and procedures. I communicated the summary of the findings upon the formal completion of the study with the participants. All transcripts, data, materials, and information related to the study are in a password-protected and encrypted external hard disk for the next 5 years, kept in a fireproof safe box with my exclusive access. I have also saved all the printed information in the same safe box. Five years after the submission of the study, I will delete the external hard drive and destroy all paper copies. In this study, I had not considered an incentive for participating.

Data Collection Instruments

The researcher is the primary instrument in the research (Castillo-Montoya, 2016; Malogon-Maldonado, 2014). I was the primary data collection instrument for this multiple case study qualitative research, collecting data through semistructured interviews and available documents. The researcher should understand the participants' experiences, as well as the participants' descriptions and interpretations of those experiences (Castillo-Montoya, 2016). To collect high-quality data, the researcher should dedicate enough time actively listening to the participants' experiences in a comfortable environment (Castillo-Montoya, 2016). The data collection of this doctoral study was through a stable and secure interview environment with the participants and the revision of the relevant documents shared by the targeted companies. I interviewed seven participants from oil service companies with no participation from the oil companies, even though I had invited them for the interviews.

Semistructured interviews could result in deeply subjective information from participants (Morse, 2015). Referring to Doody and Noonan (2013), in semistructured interviews, the researcher may explore new paths upon the emergence of any new information initially not considered in organizing the interview. While in semistructured interviews, the researcher can use a guide, altering the order of questions and including additional inquiries will be permissible (Wilson et al., 2016). As the participants are free to answer the way they wish, new ideas may emerge during semistructured interviews, allowing the researcher to further investigate those ideas through probing questions

(Wilson, 2014). Also, the open-ended questions in semistructured interviews could be

beneficial for productive dialogue in the interview process. In open-ended questions, the

participants can elaborate on their preferred responses. The mentioned characteristics of

the semistructured interviews with open-ended questions were the primary motivators of

my selection of the method.

Development of the interview protocol before starting the interview process may

result in the reliability of the study, enhancing the quality of the collected data (Castillo-

Montoya, 2016; Yin, 2018). Through an interview protocol, the researcher explains to the

participants the nature of the interview and the general format of the interview, coupled

with the statement declaring no response given to the interview questions is either right or

wrong (Doody & Noonan, 2013). The interview protocol could be a contributor to the

increased validity and reliability of the information collected in the interview process

(Yin, 2018). I have provided the interview questions in Appendix A and the interview

protocol in Appendix B.

The company's physical documents will be made available to the researcher and

are helpful for method triangulation. Researchers use the triangulation of the data sources

to identify the reliability and validity required for establishing the database while

maintaining evidence (Fusch & Ness, 2015; Yin, 2018). Researchers should evaluate

their actions, assumptions, and expectations, providing reasons for actions and decisions

required in generating results and findings of the research (Noble & Smith, 2015). The

researcher should be the custodian of the information collected, enabling other researchers to reach similar conclusions (Leung, 2015; Noble & Smith, 2015). As the

primary instrument for data collection, I ensured validity by identifying and reducing

possible biases. I minimized biases by providing an accurate and detailed summary of the

personal experiences and perspectives of the participants. I also identified the data

collection objectives, accepted custody of data, and shared the method applicable for

coding, interpretation, and analysis of the data. Upon acceptance of the participants, I

voice recorded the interviews with permission from the participants for further accuracy.

I also shared the interview transcript for validation with the participants, as required.

Data Collection Technique

This qualitative multiple case study was about the successful strategies that some

oil and gas industry leaders used to implement advanced digitalization. A deeper

exploration of participants' experiences, feelings, and thoughts may be possible through

performing interviews in a qualitative research setup (Maramwidze-Merrison, 2016). For

primary data collection, I conducted semi-structured interviews in person with the

participants over video or phone calls. A semistructured interview with open-ended

questions can result in spontaneous responses from the participants, providing the

opportunity to explore additional information during the interview process (Doody &

Noonan, 2013). The interview questions are available in Appendix A, and the interview

protocol is in Appendix B. While face-to-face interviews were preferred, I ended up

performing interviews over video or phone calls with the participants, considering the

coronavirus limitations. Referring to Seitz (2015), using a recording device can result in

more accurate data transcription. Upon obtaining permission from the participants, I voice recorded the interviews through two recording devices to ensure a backup in case of any failure in one. Then, I transferred the data to my computer in a password-protected folder.

Using reflexive analysis by paraphrasing the participants' responses during the interview is suitable for an on-spot check on the accuracy of the data (Ibrahim & Edgley, 2015). Member checking is helpful in addressing the gap in responses (Seitz, 2015). To ensure understanding of the participants' responses during the interview, I paraphrased their answers to get their feedback. I also asked probing questions. Referring to Yin (2018), probing questions during the interview could be useful in allowing the participants to enhance their responses in more detail. I also performed member checking whenever needed, providing the participants with the opportunity to review findings and conclusions after my interpretation of the collected data from their interviews. Feedback from the interviewees on the interview findings could result in further data accuracy (Fusch & Ness, 2015).

Public organizational records could be a complement to the data from interviews (Yin, 2018). I researched the public data of the participating companies as secondary data to complement the primary data I collected during or after the semistructured interviews. Method triangulation could be an enhancement to the data accuracy while facilitating a deep understanding of the phenomenon (Lodhi, 2016). Considering the recency and the confidentiality of the advanced digitalization in the oil and gas industry, the available public records on the subject were limited.

Data Organization Technique

The researcher must keep the participants' information confidential (Ummel & Achille, 2016). To protect the participants' identities, I assigned a code to each interviewee. The participants' codes in my study were P1OSC1, P2OSC1, P3OSC1, and P4OSC1 for the first company participants and P1OSC2, P2OSC2, and P3OSC2 for the second company participants. In the mentioned coding, P was the person, and OSC was the oil service company. Therefore, I am the only one knowing the identity of the participants. During the interviews, I recorded the interviews using two digital recorders. After the interviews, I transcribed the semistructured interviews.

To ensure consistency, the researcher must categorize and label the collected data (Marshall & Rossman, 2016; Ranney et al., 2015). I used NVivo to code the study data to identify and categorize emerging themes. I also kept reflective journals and research logs to track my thinking process, observations, codings, classifications, and data analysis. I stored the digital copies of the interview recordings, Excel spreadsheets, reflective journals, and research logs on a password-protected external hard drive. I will lock the hard drive and any other documents relevant to the study, including hard copies of any research-related data, in a safe box only accessible to me. Upon completing 5 years after the conclusion of the doctoral study, I will shred all hard copies and delete all soft documents and recordings.

Data Analysis

A researcher performs data analysis for data preparation, organization, and categorization into themes used to interpret the findings (Saunders et al., 2016). In the case studies, researchers apply method triangulation to multiple information sources to draw research conclusions (Morse, 2015; Patton, 2015; Yin, 2018). Method triangulation may be an improvement to the collected data from interviews by bridging the existing gaps and increasing data validity (Bekhet & Zauszniewski, 2012; Yin, 2018). Referring to Baškarada et al. (2017), achieving method triangulation may be an assistant to the realization of data saturation. I used method triangulation in my research. In data collection for my doctoral study, I used semistructured interviews and the company's public documents and information. The researcher should analyze the collected data from different sources. The researcher may use software packages for searching and analyzing text-based data and coding (Woods et al., 2016). I used NVivo, a data analysis software, to comprehensively analyze the collected data.

The researcher addresses the research question through a logical and sequential data analysis process by utilizing relevant analysis techniques for qualitative research (Vaismoradi et al., 2016). The data analysis process comprises (a) reduction, (b) delineation, (c) clusterization, (d) validation, and (e) theme extraction (Groenewald, 2004). The objective of the reduction phase is to minimize the researcher's influence on the data collection process by setting aside the researcher's presuppositions (Groenewald, 2004). Referring to Yin (2018), the researcher may avoid biases by acknowledging them towards the phenomenon under study. The objective of the delineation phase is to extract the relevant information from each interview into different categories (Groenewald, 2004). In the clusterization phase, the researcher combines related categories to create themes. The objective of the validation phase is to perform a validity check with the participants on the core synthesis of each associated interview (Groenewald, 2004). In the theme extraction phase, the researcher creates a summary of the extracted themes from all interviews. In this doctoral research, I followed the method provided by Groenewald (2004) while using NVivo for detailed data analysis. I identified the predetermined themes in my doctoral research as strategic change and its interrelated factors, which were my study's conceptual design components. The predetermined themes were (a) strategic change, (b) environmental assessment, (c) required resources, (d) linking strategic and operational changes, (e) leading change, and (f) overall coherence (Pettigrew & Whipp, 1993; Sminia, 2021). I determined the final themes after performing data analysis for my doctoral research.

Reliability and Validity

Referring to Morse (2015), the rigor of qualitative research is dependent on reliability and validity, achievable through truthfulness, integrity, and credibility of the study. Evaluation of the qualitative research includes evaluation of (a) dependability, (b) credibility, (c) transferability, and (d) confirmability (Erlingsson & Brysiewicz, 2013). In quantitative research, internal and external validities are essential (Lewis, 2015). Considering my research was qualitative, internal and external validities were not relevant.

Reliability

In reliable research, future researchers should reach the same findings if replicating the study (Cypress, 2017; Yin, 2018). Using multiple data sources should be an enhancement to the reliability of the case study (Ridder, 2017). To improve the reliability of qualitative research, the researcher should document the steps and procedures applied in the research (Morse, 2015). An interview protocol providing a procedural guide in conducting the interviews may result in improvement of the reliability (Gesch-Karamanlidis, 2015). Dependability is achievable through precise documentation of data collection and organization processes, as well as member checking of the analyzed data for participants' feedback (Frels & Onwuegbuzie, 2013).

In my doctoral study, I applied several methods to ensure readers' ability to monitor and verify the reliability of the overall research. The first method was collecting data from interviews with participants, reviewing public documents of the participating companies, and receiving feedback on the interview transcripts from the participants. The second method was a frequent reassessment of the research notes using critical and reflective thinking to minimize the introduction of bias into the study. The third method was tracking the collected data from different sources to demonstrate data management, coding, categorization, and analysis in a detailed log.

Validity

Credibility

Referring to Fusch and Ness (2015), the trustworthiness of the researcher's conclusions could be the identifier of the research credibility. The recording of the interview is an assurance of the data transcription accuracy (Yin, 2018). During the interview, the researcher may paraphrase the participants' responses to ensure understanding through reflexive analysis (Ibrahim & Edgley, 2015). After the interview transcription, the participants will have the opportunity to verify their responses to improve credibility (Fusch & Ness, 2015). The use of triangulation may be helpful in addressing the gap in the collected data, increasing data saturation (Erlingsson & Brysiewicz, 2013). I applied reflexive analysis, voice recording, member checking, and data triangulation to assure the credibility of my research.

Transferability

Transferability is the ability to transfer a phenomenon at a specific condition to other similar conditions (Noble & Smith, 2015). Referring to Leung (2015), the assessment of the transferability of the research may be achievable through constant comparison, auditing, and documentation. A researcher should equip readers with a detailed description of the study to provide the readers with the ability to evaluate the transferability of the research (Morse, 2015). I maintained a journal during the interview and the data collection process to allow readers to assess my study's transferability.

Confirmability

Referring to Ibrahim and Edgley (2015), the researcher may demonstrate the confirmability of the research with an unbiased, objective approach. Ibrahim and Edgley (2015) suggested track-keeping of the interviewer's thoughts during the data collection process to identify possible biases. Data collection through multiple data sources could result in improvement of data confirmability through triangulation (Denzin, 2012). I ensured my research's confirmability through data triangulation and writing my personal biases and preconceived notions in a reflexive journal.

In a qualitative study, data saturation is an indicator of the research accuracy, validity, and confirmability (Fusch & Ness, 2015). The authors confirm data saturation when new data, themes, and codes stop emerging, and the replication of the study becomes achievable. In a case study, the researcher explores different data sources within the case study's parameters to assure data saturation (Yin, 2018). There is a direct connection between data triangulation and data saturation (Fusch & Ness, 2015).

Transition and Summary

In Section 2, I restated the purpose statement for this qualitative multiple case study in exploring successful strategies that some leaders in the oil and gas industry used to implement advanced digitalization. Section 2 also contained the role of the researcher, the participants, the research method and design, the population and sampling, the data collection instruments, the data collection technique, and the data organization technique. Besides, I included the strategy and tools for ensuring an ethical, reliable, and valid research study. I prepared Section 3 after conducting my study. Section 3 contains the study's findings and conclusions with their implications for social change. I have also provided recommendations for further studies.

Section 3: Application to Professional Practice and Implications for Change

Introduction

The purpose of this qualitative multiple case study was to explore successful strategies some leaders in the oil and gas industry used to implement advanced digitalization. All research participants considered advanced digitalization the way forward in the oil and gas industry. They also predicted fast progress of advanced digitalization in the oil and gas industry in the next few years. I administered seven semistructured interviews in a relaxed environment for the participants to receive detailed responses to the seven interview questions (see Appendix A). Through a combination of interview data, a review of publicly available documents, a comprehensive literature review, and a conceptual framework, I identified the strategies used by participants for the successful implementation of advanced digitalization in the oil and gas industry. Analysis of the results revealed six themes: (a) successful advanced digitalization strategies divided into content or what, process or how, and context or where for strategic change; (b) environmental assessment divided into regulatory, economic, and industrial; (c) resources divided into the structure, process, and people; (d) linking strategic and operational changes divided into potential benefits and potential challenges; (e) leading advanced digitalization change focused on the indicators; and (f) overall coherence of advanced digitalization divided into adoption and requirements. The results of this study support Pettigrew and Whipp's (1993) dimensions of strategic change conceptual framework. In the following section of this report, I have confirmed the relation between the themes described and extracted from the data collected and the conceptual framework.

Presentation of the Findings

The overarching research question was "What successful advanced digitalization strategies can leaders in the oil and gas industry use to implement digitalization?" I examined this question through the lens of Pettigrew and Whipp's dimensions of strategic change (1993) conceptual framework. Seven advanced digitalization leaders from two oil service companies participated in the study. I conducted data analysis through thematic analysis and coding of the transcribed interviews. The researcher can identify trends or common themes through thematic analysis of qualitative data that provides valuable knowledge about the research question (Moira & Brid, 2017). The six emergent themes for the upstream oil and gas were (a) advanced digitalization strategies, including what, how, and where; (b) environmental assessment including regulatory, economic, and industrial; (c) resources including structure, process, and people; (d) linking strategical and operational changes; (e) leading change; and (f) overall coherence. Pettigrew and Whipp's dimensions of strategic change align with the findings, existing literature, and themes.

It is worth considering that all participants were involved in upstream and specifically drilling from two oil service companies instead of the previously planned one oil company and one oil service company. Therefore, this section mainly focuses on upstream from the oil service companies' perspective. Even though I had invited potential participants from oil companies to the interviews, they did not participate in this study due to the tightness of the oil and gas industry in sharing data, especially for oil companies. Regardless of no participation from oil companies, I still collected as much data as possible regarding the oil companies' perspective on advanced digitalization in interviewing the oil service company participants. I asked interviewees to answer the interview questions from the perspectives of an oil service company as well as an oil company, given the close collaboration and understanding between oil companies and oil service companies in developing and implementing advanced digitalization solutions. With this approach, there may be some valuable findings for the oil companies as well as the oil service companies in this study. I have presented the word cloud of frequency query results from interviews in Figure 1.

Figure 1

Word Cloud of Frequency Query Result from the Interviews

Emergent Theme 1: Advanced Digitalization Strategies

The first theme that emerged from the data collection process was the advanced digitalization strategies (see Table 4). The strategies shared by the participants covered the dimension of strategic change, including content (what), process (how), and context

(where). The participants explained what strategies they used and how and where they

used them. Analyzing the participants' responses entered into NVivo 12 made it evident

that the participants regarded the advanced digitalization strategies as a top priority in the

advanced digitalization journey. Table 4 shows the frequency of participants' comments

concerning advanced digitalization strategies. Table 5 is a detailed review of the findings

broken down into the dimensions of advanced digitalization strategies: what, how, and

where. I provide detailed subcategories under each dimension of advanced digitalization

strategies, the number of times each subcategory came up, and the number of participants

referred to each subcategory during the interviews. The number of participants discussed

each of the subcategories was more than one, showing data saturation.

Table 4

Emergent Theme 1: Number of Times Advanced Digitalization Strategies Discussed

Interview Participant	Number of Times the Theme Emerged in the Interview	Percentage of Contribution to Emergent Theme
P1OSC1	30	14%
P2OSC1	23	11%
P3OSC1	36	17%
P4OSC1	25	12%
P1OSC2	30	14%
P2OSC2	26	12%
P3OSC2	46	21%
Total	216	100%

Table 5

Emergent of Subcategories for Theme 1

Dimensions of advanced digitalization strategies	Subcategories	# of times subcategory emerged	# of participants referred to subcategory	% of subcategory emergence
What	Goal of Advanced Digitalization	9	7	4%
What	Dynamic Nature / Journey / Fast-Changing Landscape	9	6	4%
What	Focus on Customers' Priorities	5	5	2%
What	Multi-Stakeholder Envolvement	8	7	4%
What	Internal versus External	5	5	2%
What	Data-Centric	9	5	4%
What	Digital Platform, Software, Cloud	10	6	5%
What	Implementation / Management of Change / Top-Down or Bottom-Up	11	7	5%
What	Success Criteria	9	7	4%
What	Adoption (Internal versus External)	7	7	3%
How	Learning from Other Industries / Using Available Tools	8	4	4%
How	Fit-for-Purpose / Scalable	7	6	3%
How	Full Customer Involvement (Engagement / Partnership)	6	4	3%
How	Focused on Users / User-Interface Centric	7	4	3%
How	Agility in Addressing Requirements and Feedbacks	6	4	3%
How	Transparency with User if User Replacement by Digital Planned	4	3	2%
How	Full Organization Commitment / Reinforcement for Digital	3	3	1%
How	Adopt Digital Mindset	4	4	2%
How	Integration / Removing Silos between Stakeholders for Seamless Flow	7	6	3%
How	Thorough Advanced Digital Introduction to Users	6	5	3%
How	Expandable Open Advanced Digital Solution for All Stakeholders	6	5	3%

(table continues)

Dimensions of advanced digitalization strategies	Subcategories	# of times subcategory emerged	# of participants referred to subcategory	% of subcategory emergence
How	Open Mindset and Flexibility with Advanced Digital Solutions	6	5	3%
How	Support Users during Application of Advanced Digital Solution for Smooth Transitioning	6	6	3%
How	Training / Education / Communication on Advanced Digital Solution	12	6	6%
How	The capture of Existing Workflows in Advanced Digital Solution	4	4	2%
How	Continuous Improvement of Advanced Digital Strategy and Solution	8	6	4%
Where	Upstream / Drilling / Oil Service Company	7	7	3%
Where	Early Stage / Infancy of Advanced Digital	7	7	3%
Where	With Customers Receptive / Cooperative / Believer in Advanced Digital	3	3	1%
Where	In Collaboration with Stakeholders for Interoperability of Solution	9	7	4%
Where	In COVID-19 Pandemic	8	7	4%
Total		216	7	100%

Emergent Theme 2: Environment Assessment

The second theme that emerged from the data collection process was the environmental assessment, including regulatory, economic, and industrial. Analyzing the participants' responses entered into NVivo 12, the importance of environmental assessment was evident. Table 6 shows the frequency of participants' comments concerning environmental assessment. Table 7 is a detailed review of the findings broken down into categories of environmental assessment: economic, industrial, and regulatory. I provide detailed subcategories under the category of environmental assessment, the number of times each subcategory came up, and the number of participants referred to each subcategory during the interviews. The number of participants discussed each subcategory was more than one, showing data saturation.

Table 6

Emergent Theme 2: Number of Times Environmental Assessment Discussed

Interview Participant	Number of Times the Theme Emerged in the Interview	Percentage of Contribution to Emergent Theme
P1OSC1	15	16%
P2OSC1	12	13%
P3OSC1	12	13%
P4OSC1	19	21%
P1OSC2	11	12%
P2OSC2	13	14%
P3OSC2	10	11%
Total	92	100%

Table 7

Emergent of Subcategories for Theme 2

Environmental assessment categories	Subcategories	# of times subcategory emerged	# of participants referred to subcategory	% of subcategory emergence
Economic	Covid - Capex Constrained	5	4	5%
Industrial	Data Management - Restricted Data-Sharing / Restricted Processes	10	5	11%
Industrial	Digital Era - Increase in Adoption of Advanced Digitalization	11	7	12%
Industrial	Existence of Legacy Business Systems and Technologies	7	5	8%
Industrial	Digital Era - Advanced Digital Infancy in Oil and Gas Industry	7	5	8%
Industrial	Cloud - Open Platform for Leveraging Data	9	6	10%
Industrial	Progress in Big Data / Data Lakes	5	3	5%
Industrial	High Risk Industry - Health / Safety / Environment	4	3	4%
Industrial	Complicated Multi-Stakeholder Environment Lacking Integration	13	7	14%
Industrial	Heavily Operated by Hardwares - Drilling Rigs, Drilling Tools	3	3	3%
Industrial	Oil and Gas Industry with Aging Population, Approaching Its Expiry Date	2	2	2%
Regulatory	Lack of Regulations - Cybersecurity, and Intellectual Property Ownership	4	3	4%
Regulatory	Unfavorable Regulations - Data Residency	6	5	7%
Regulatory	Covid - Requirement to Work Remotely	6	4	7%
Total		92	7	100%

Emergent Theme 3: Advanced Digitalization Resources

The third theme that emerged from the data collection process was required

resources for advanced digitalization consisting of structure, process, and people.

Analyzing the participants' responses entered into NVivo 12, the required resources for

advanced digitalization were evident. Table 8 is about the frequency of participants'

comments concerning advanced digitalization resources. Table 9 is a detailed review of

the findings broken down into categories of advanced digitalization resources: structure,

process, and people. I have provided detailed subcategories under the category of

advanced digitalization resources, the number of times each subcategory came up, and

the number of participants referred to each subcategory during the interviews. The

number of participants discussed each subcategory was more than one, showing data

saturation.

Table 8

Emergent Theme 3: Number of Times Advanced Digitalization Resources Discussed

Interview Participant	Number of Times the Theme Emerged in the Interview	Percentage of Contribution to Emergent Theme
P1OSC1	8	15%
P2OSC1	9	17%
P3OSC1	6	11%
P4OSC1	8	15%
P1OSC2	11	21%
P2OSC2	5	9%
P3OSC2	6	11%
Total	53	100%

Table 9

Emergent of Subcategories for Theme 3

Advanced digitalization resources categories	Subcategories	# of times subcategory emerged	# of participants referred to subcategory	%of subcategory emergence
People	Experts for Development, Implementation, and Support Teams (In-House or Outsourced)	7	6	13%
People	Advanced Digitalization Adopters and Users (Oil Companies, Drilling Contractors, etc)	5	5	9%
People / Process	Education and Training of Workforce on Advanced Digital (In-House or Outsourced)	7	6	13%
Process	Advanced Digitalization Capital Investment / Budget	5	4	9%
Process	Advanced Digitalization Compatible Regulations and Standards (Cybersecurity, Data Residency, etc)	7	5	13%
Process	Advanced Digitalization Roadmap / Implementation Plan / KPIs / Incentives / Communications	8	7	15%
Structure	Advanced Digitalization Platform (Cloud, Software, Storage Capacity, Bandwidth, etc) (Owned or Outsourced)	8	6	15%
Structure	Advanced Digital Compatible Rigs and Tools	6	6	11%
Total		53	7	100%

Emergent Theme 4: Linking Strategic and Operational Changes of Advanced Digitalization

The fourth theme that emerged from the data collection process was linking strategic and operational changes through potential benefits and challenges of advanced digitalization. I have summarized the analysis of the participants' responses entered into NVivo 12 related to linking strategic and operational changes of advanced digitalization in Table 10 and Table 11. Table 10 is about the frequency of participants' comments concerning Theme 4. Table 11 is a detailed review of the findings broken down into categories linking strategic and operational changes of advanced digitalization: potential benefits and challenges. I have provided detailed subcategories of potential benefits and challenges under Theme 4, the number of times each subcategory came up, and the number of participants referred to each subcategory during the interviews. The number of participants discussed each subcategory was more than one, showing data saturation.

Table 10

Emergent Theme 4: Number of Times Linking Strategic and Operational Changes Discussed

Interview Participant	Number of Times the Theme Emerged in the Interview	Percentage of Contribution to Emergent Theme
P1OSC1	18	14%
P2OSC1	19	15%
P3OSC1	20	16%
P4OSC1	23	18%
P1OSC2	14	11%
P2OSC2	15	12%
P3OSC2	17	13%
Total	126	100%

Table 11

Emergent of Subcategories for Theme 4

Environmental assessment categories	Subcategories	# of times subcategory emerged	# of participants referred to subcategory	% of subcategory emergence
Potential Benefit	Improved Performance, Improved Efficiency	7	5	6%
Potential Benefit	Reduced Cost of $/ft or Reduced Cost of $/bbl of Oil	5	4	4%
Potential Benefit	Covid - Advanced Digitalization Facilitated Working Remotely	6	4	5%
Potential Benefit	Visibility (Real-Time) through connectivity, Leveraging Expertise for Decision Making	3	3	2%
Potential Benefit	Procedural Adherence, Consistency in Results (Sustainability), Standardization	5	4	4%
Potential Benefit	Reduction of Safety Risks and Environmental Risks	4	2	3%
Potential Challenge	Difficulty Measuring Effectiveness of Advanced Digital / Lack of Agreed Indicators	5	4	4%
Potential Challenge	Human Resistance in shifting from Manual or Legacy Technology to Digital	14	6	11%
Potential Challenge	Lack of Relevant Standards for Advanced Digitalization in the Oil and Gas Industry	6	4	5%
Potential Challenge	Existence of Regulations Slowing Advanced Digitalization (Data Residency)	5	5	4%
Potential Challenge	Industry Closeness in Data / Process Sharing among Stakeholders, Lack of Integration	18	7	14%
Potential Challenge	Covid - Capex Constrained	4	3	3%

(table continues)

Environmental assessment categories	Subcategories	# of times subcategory emerged	# of participants referred to subcategory	% of subcategory emergence
Potential Challenge	Requirement of Fit-for-Purpose Solution - No Universal Solution	9	6	7%
Potential Challenge	Setting the Expectation of Customers and Users on Advanced Digital	3	3	2%
Potential Challenge	Dynamic, Fast-Evolving Environment with Advanced Digitalization	5	5	4%
Potential Challenge	Developing / Training Workforce / Customers for Advanced Digitalization Competency	10	6	8%
Potential Challenge	Existence of Drilling Rigs and Tools Incompatible with Advanced Digitalization	3	3	2%
Potential Challenge	Users' Fear of Losing Their Jobs after Advanced Digitalization	7	7	6%
Potential Challenge	High-Cost Critical Industry - Resistance Against Disruptive Solutions - Short Lifetime - Aging Population	7	3	6%
Total		92	7	100%

Emergent Theme 5: Leading Advanced Digitalization in the Oil and Gas Industry

The fifth theme from the data collection process was leading the advanced digitalization change in the oil and gas industry. I have summarized the analysis of the participants' responses entered into NVivo 12 related to leading the advanced digitalization change in Table 12 and Table 13. Table 12 is associated with the frequency of participants' comments concerning Theme 5. Table 13 is a detailed review of the findings under the main category: the indicators of leading the change. I have provided detailed subcategories under Theme 5, the number of times each subcategory came up, and the number of participants referred to each subcategory during the interviews. The number of participants discussed each subcategory was more than one, showing data saturation.

Table 12

Emergent Theme 5: Number of Times Leading Advance Digitalization in the Oil and Gas Industry Discussed

Interview Participant	Number of Times the Theme Emerged in the Interview	Percentage of Contribution to Emergent Theme
P1OSC1	8	13%
P2OSC1	11	18%
P3OSC1	7	11%
P4OSC1	11	18%
P1OSC2	9	15%
P2OSC2	7	11%
P3OSC2	9	15%
Total	62	100%

Table 13

Emergent of Subcategories for Theme 5

Leading advanced digitalization categories	Subcategories	# of times subcategory emerged	# of participants referred to subcategory	% of subcategory emergence
Indicator	Developing Advanced Digital Solutions for Internal Use and/or for Early Adopters	7	7	11%
Indicator	Training and Development of the Workforce and Stakeholders on Advanced Digital	7	6	11%
Indicator	Embracement of Advanced Digital Internally throughout Different Organizations	4	4	6%
Indicator	Building on Other Industries' Learnings on Advanced Digital	7	5	11%
Indicator	Experiencing Resistance towards Advanced Digitalization from Different Stakeholders	7	6	11%
Indicator	Working Around Unfavorable Standards, Regulations, and siloed Organizations	11	6	18%
Indicator	Developing Indicators and Track Record to Show Benefits of Advanced Digital	7	6	11%
Indicator	Dealing with Drilling Rigs and Tools Not Fully Compatible with Advanced Digital	5	5	8%
Indicator	Addressing Resistance towards Change through Management of Change Process	7	5	11%
Total		62	7	100%

Emergent Theme 6: Overall Coherence of Advanced Digital in the Oil and Gas Industry

The sixth theme from the data collection process was the overall coherence of advanced digitalization in the oil and gas industry. I have summarized the analysis of the participants' responses entered into NVivo 12 related to the overall coherence of the advanced digitalization change in Table 14 and Table 15. Table 14 is associated with the frequency of participants' comments concerning Theme 6. Table 15 is a detailed review of the findings broken down into adoption and requirements. I have provided detailed subcategories under Theme 6, the number of times each subcategory came up, and the number of participants referred to each subcategory during the interviews. The number of participants discussed each subcategory was more than one, showing data saturation.

Table 14

Emergent Theme 6: Number of Times Overall Coherence of Advance Digitalization in the Oil and Gas Industry Discussed

Interview Participant	Number of Times the Theme Emerged in the Interview	Percentage of Contribution to Emergent Theme
P1OSC1	11	17%
P2OSC1	9	14%
P3OSC1	8	12%
P4OSC1	11	17%
P1OSC2	9	14%
P2OSC2	10	15%
P3OSC2	7	11%
Total	65	100%

Table 15

Emergent of Subcategories for Theme 6: Number of Times Different Subcategories for Theme 6 Emerged in Relation with the Number of Participants Discussed Those Subcategories

Overall Coherence of Advanced Digitalization Categories	Subcategories	Number of Times Subcategory Emerged	Number of Participants Referred to Subcategory	Percentage of Subcategory Emergence
Adoption	Substantial Progress of Advanced Digitalization in Oil and Gas Industry (Next 5 Years)	7	7	11%
Adoption	New Generation More Inclined towards Advance Digitalization	2	2	3%
Requirement	Openness in Safe Data and Process Sharing with Stakeholders - Avoiding Silos	8	6	12%
Requirement	Collaboration and Integration of the Stakeholders - Change of Mindset	3	3	5%
Requirement	Increased Number of Competent Workforce and Stakeholders on Advanced Digital	6	6	9%
Requirement	Continue Training and Education on Advanced Digital	8	6	12%
Requirement	Increased Number of Drilling Rigs and Tools Compatible with Advanced Digitalization	5	5	8%
Requirement	Developed Track Record of Advanced Digitalization Benefits Through Agreed Indicators	4	4	6%
Requirement	Mapping Benefits of Advanced Digital for	7	6	11%

Overall Coherence of Advanced Digitalization Categories	Subcategories	Number of Times Subcategory Emerged	Number of Participants Referred to Subcategory	Percentage of Subcategory Emergence
	Different User Categories			
Requirement	Increased Number of Standards and Regulations Compatible with Advanced Digitalization	8	6	12
Requirement	Career Mapping for the Users after Advanced Digitalizing - Overcome Fear of Digital	7	6	11
Total		65	7	100%

Applications to Professional Practice

The outcome of this study in implementing advanced digitalization may result in positive economic benefits while minimizing risks, as analyzed under Theme 4, which was linking strategic and operational change. Implementation of advanced digitalization in the upstream oil and gas industry may result in further reliability of operations through procedural adherence, consistency, sustainability of results, and standardization. Also, in this study, the importance of standards and regulations compatible with advanced digitalization has been discussed, which could result in safer data sharing with fewer cybersecurity vulnerabilities. Additionally, this study may be suitable for further gaining the trust of the companies in the oil and gas industry for embarking on the advanced digitalization journey for their upstream operations.

Implications for Social Change

This study might result in a positive social change by providing more reliable practices for leaders performing advanced digitalization operations in the oil and gas industry. The findings of this study could be suitable for expediting the transformation of the oil and gas industry, resulting in more job opportunities for residents of the communities. The lower the cost of the services, the more opportunities for drilling more wells, which may result in increased work opportunities. This study may result in more local financial stability through strengthened business activities, improving human or social conditions by promoting the community's worth, dignity, and development. This study could lead to enhanced local lifestyles and the well-being of local communities, stimulating economic prosperity.

Recommendations for Action

The purpose of this qualitative multiple case study was to explore successful strategies some leaders in the oil and gas industry used to implement advanced digitalization. There were six themes in the research findings. The recommendation in action is related to the cruciality of having a strategy for migration to advanced digitalization. There could be changes to the strategy over time. Therefore, the oil and gas digital leaders must keep an open mind for fine-tuning the initial strategy. The oil and gas industry leaders at different stages of the digitalization process, planning, execution, and evaluation, could explore the findings of this study for their successful migration to digital oil and gas. The results of this study indicated that the benefits of advanced digitalization are evident. At the same time, the robust statistics quantifying the benefits are not yet fully available, considering the digital recency in the oil and gas industry. While the benefits are not quantified, the challenges of advanced digitalization are real. The companies should have the right strategy for a successful migration to digital.

The findings of this study are potentially invaluable to the oil and gas industry leaders, learning from the success of the early adopters of advanced digitalization in the oil and gas sector. Rose and Flynn (2018) explained that researchers must disseminate research findings to influence policies and managerial practices. This study will later be reviewed by scholars, leaders, and students in the ProQuest database. I will also provide all participants with a summary of the findings and recommendations. If needed, I will also be willing to discuss the results at conferences and forums. I will publish a journal article on this study to reach other people interested in this doctoral study.

Recommendations for Further Research

Greener (2018) explained that the researcher could use limitations to identify and recommend future research topics. Referring to Tortorella et al. (2020), the companies should get involved in creating, retaining, and transferring the knowledge related to Industry 4.0 technologies within their organizations to remain competitive. Advanced digitalization is essential in today's world for every industry. The findings of this study could result in further research, especially considering the recency of advanced digitalization in the oil and gas industry, restricting the availability of potential participants for the interview process holding sharable information. Furthermore, data confidentiality in the oil and gas industry corporations has been a traditional roadblock, affecting the research outcome in this domain.

This research was limited to the oil and gas companies with successful advanced digitalization strategies in North America. Even though the plan was to interview participants from both oil service companies and oil companies, I did not manage to secure interviews with the oil company participants regardless of lengthy and intense follow-ups. The lack of interviews with oil company participants limited the study and restricted the transferability of the findings. I recommend expanding this study with the inclusion of participants from oil companies. Future researchers could include participants from more extensive geography than only North America. The sample size for this study was adequate to attain saturation.

Future researchers may refer to this study's emergent themes to identify additional research areas. Additional research may be possible by applying different conceptual frameworks, theories, methodologies, and designs to gather and analyze participant data on successful advanced digitalization strategies in the oil and gas industry. Finally, potential researchers may explore the inverse of this study and analyze unsuccessful strategies in advanced digitalization in the oil and gas industry.

Reflections

The Doctor of Business Administration (DBA) program at Walden University has improved my time management, persistence, self-discipline, and focus. While achieving a doctorate's high academic expectations is demanding, it nurtures perseverance, dedication, and tenacity. Through my doctoral study, I have acquired considerable knowledge of digitalization in different industries, primarily focusing on the oil and gas industry. I found the importance of the right strategies for successfully implementing advanced digitalization in the oil and gas industry. It has been challenging to stay away

from biases with my experience in the oil and gas industry. Throughout the doctoral

study, I learned to open-mindedly focus on the participant's point of view. I am fully

aware that the effect of knowledge sharing in facilitating faster learning is significant.

Therefore, I consider all challenges during the research process, mainly due to

information-sharing complications in the oil and gas industry, worthwhile. I remain

grateful for the seven digitalization leaders who shared their successful advanced

digitalization strategies for this research. Regardless of their busy work schedules, the

participants joined this research without personal prejudices or preconceived values. I

believe the learning experience throughout this doctoral study will be helpful for me on

the way forward as a scholar-researcher. I remain motivated with the desire to extend my

research after the completion of this program.

Conclusion

I used a qualitative multiple case study to explore the successful strategies some

oil and gas industry leaders used to implement advanced digitalization. For this research,

I interviewed seven digitalization leaders in the US oil and gas service companies with

successful digitalization strategies. I also collected data using methodological

triangulation until reaching data saturation. Data analysis consisted of NVivo 12,

recorded transcripts, and member checking to confirm the participants' accurate

responses. This study resulted in a list of successful strategies for implementing advanced

digitalization in the upstream oil and gas industry, along with the proper implementation

process and related requirements. This study showed that advanced digitalization is the future for the oil and gas industry, like many other industries. The transformation journey has started in the industry, and it is expected to see an acceleration in the progress of advanced digitalization. The findings may also help create more jobs by lowering the cost of provided services and the cost per barrel of oil produced. There could be more interest in drilling more wells if the costs are lower than in the past. The findings of this study may foster positive social change by creating more jobs and making companies more resilient in the face of industry downturns.

Milton Keynes UK
Ingram Content Group UK Ltd.
UKHW020822191223
434651UK00014B/700